WOMEN
AND
AIDS

The Continuum Counseling Series

WOMEN AND AIDS

A Practical Guide for Those Who Help Others

Bonnie Lester

Foreword by William Van Ornum

Continuum | New York

For Sebastian and Carmelo

1989

The Continuum Publishing Company
370 Lexington Avenue
New York, NY 10017

Printed in the United States of America

Library of Congress Cataloging-in-Publication Data

Lester, Bonnie.
    Women and AIDS : a practical guide for those who help others /
Bonnie Lester ; foreword by William Van Ornum.
        p.   cm. — (The Continuum counseling series)
    ISBN 0-8264-0501-0
    1. AIDS (Disease)—Psychological aspects. 2. Women—Counseling
of. 3. Women—Diseases. 4. AIDS phobia.   I. Title.   II. Series.
RC607.A26L473 1989
616.97'92—dc19   88-31910
                                                                CIP

Contents

Contents

Foreword

The Continuum Counseling Series—the first of its kind for a wide audience—presents books for everyone interested in counseling, bringing to readers practical counseling handbooks that include real-life approaches from current research. The topics deal with issues that are of concern to each of us, our families, friends, acquaintances, or colleagues at work.

General readers, parents, teachers, social workers, psychologists, school counselors, nurses and doctors, pastors, and others in helping fields too numerous to mention will welcome these guidebooks that combine the best professional learnings and common sense, written by practicing counselors with expertise in their specialty.

Increased understanding of ourselves and others is a primary goal of these books—and all professionals agree that greater empathy is the quality essential to effective counseling. Each book offers practical suggestions on how to "talk with" others about the theme of the book—be this in an informal and spontaneous conversation or in a more formal counseling session.

Professional therapists will value these books also, because each volume in The Continuum Counseling Series develops its subject in a unified way, unlike many other books that may be either too technical or, as edited collections of papers, may come across as being disjointed. In recent years both the American Psychological Association and the American Psychiatric Association have endorsed books that build on the scientific traditions of each profession but are communicated in an interesting way to general readers. We hope that professors and students in fields such as psychology, social work, psychiatry, guidance and counseling, and other helping fields will find these books to be helpful companion readings for undergraduate and graduate courses.

From nonprofessional counselors to professional therapists, from students of psychology to interested lay readers, The Continuum Counseling Series endeavors to provide informative, interesting, and useful tools for everyone who cares about learning and dealing more effectively with these universal, human concerns.

Women and AIDS

Bonnie Lester recognizes the power of AIDS to frighten and repel us. She is interested in how AIDS affects women, a focus of her work and this book.

Much of counseling is inspired by the counselor's own awareness of similar experiences and reflection upon these. Bonnie Lester reveals her own struggles as a close friend died of AIDS, and how this experience has inspired her to work with other helpers to make them more effective.

Women and AIDS will be of interest to women and anyone who works with them in a counseling capacity. Feelings engendered by AIDS are discussed in detail, and there is a helpful primer outlining essential facts currently known about the disease. An important part of the book involves numerous interviews that Bonnie has conducted with women themselves, including an extended discussion with a woman diagnosed with AIDS seven years ago. While realizing that there is no "cookbook approach" to counseling, she presents many useful and practical ideas in chapters devoted to "Counseling Issues: Talking to Women about AIDS" and "Women Talking to Children about AIDS."

Bonnie Lester's portrayal of the death of her friend Sebastian, and her own self-disclosure and counseling expertise, will enable readers to understand and deal more effectively with AIDS, particularly as it affects women.

William Van Ornum, Ph.D.
Marist College
Poughkeepsie, New York

General Editor
The Continuum Counseling Series

Acknowledgments

I wish to thank all those who contributed to this book by providing interviews, resources, encouragement, moral support, and assisting with the typing of the manuscript: Harriet Forman Barrett, Sandy Callahan, Charlotte Frank, Chris Hellin, Nikodim Janusev, Michael Leach, Evander Lomke, Margie, Christine Sarafoff, Michelle Tuchman, Ethel Turner, as well as the many women who took the time to answer questionnaries and grant interviews.

I would also like to thank my father, Albert Lester, who many years ago attempted to instill confidence in me and my ability to express myself on paper.

I am especially grateful to William Van Ornum who had faith in my writing and held my hand through every stage of this book. Thank you, Bill!

Introduction

This book is for nonprofessional and professional counselors—ranging from teachers to social workers to psychologists—who become involved not only with women who get AIDS, but with people who react to others who have AIDS. Before we can become effective helpers, we must learn to confront our feelings and fears that surround the AIDS issues.

As a therapist who counsels and presents lectures on AIDS, I often find that my feelings help me to make direct and honest connections with others but can also interfere with my effectiveness.

The most painful and devastating experience in my life was the loss of a dear and long-time friend, who died three years ago at the age of thirty-nine, as a result of an AIDS-related opportunistic infection. After Sebastian's death, I realized how little I knew about this new and fatal disease. My ignorance was a result of prior lack of personal involvement with AIDS. I had read newspaper and magazine articles about the unique disease that seemed to have an affinity for the male homosexual population, but had no concern that it would touch my life. How wrong I was.

As we now realize, AIDS is not solely a homosexual disease. It has entered into the general population, infecting men, women, and children, regardless of race, country, or religion. It is the number one killer of men *and* women in New York City who are between the ages of twenty and forty-nine. Babies born with AIDS are increasing in number. In several central African countries, more than one-third of the general population is infected with the AIDS virus.

Even people who are well educated in regard to the AIDS epidemic are afraid. Seasoned and professional nurses have panicked when a person with AIDS is admitted to their unit. Experienced school guidance counselors become afraid to hug a hemophiliac child infected through transfusions. Panic and unrealistic fear about AIDS are becoming a common characteristic of our society.

It may be that publishers feel that there have been enough books written about AIDS. There has been a plethora of books on AIDS . . . 140 new books in 1987 alone, according to a recent survey in *Publisher's Weekly*. Nearly all these books stress the medical facts or how to prevent AIDS. This book is unique in providing a look at women and AIDS. It also stresses positive approaches for all helpers who must confront AIDS not only in its victims but in the reaction of others. Practical counseling suggestions, not only talking to women with AIDS but talking to women about AIDS, are presented. If we are to be empathetic helpers, it is important that we know the core issues that women with AIDS must face.

Much of the book presents original interview data on how women from a range of professions—nurses, teachers, writers, social workers—have dealt with AIDS with compassion not only for the victims but with sensitivity toward the reactions of colleagues who often panic when learning a person with AIDS will be enrolled in their school, their hospital unit, or their company.

Any discussion about AIDS ultimately involves talking about sexuality, death, and morality. Most women are not comfortable talking openly about these issues. Here are guidelines to help women discuss AIDS on all levels with their children, family, and each other.

This book will introduce many women who have experiences and feelings to share about AIDS. In some instances, names and circumstances of individuals have been changed at their request, but these women all want to share actual experiences in order to help others that are living in the era of heartbreak and devastation surrounding AIDS.

An attempt to look at AIDS from a women's viewpoint is presented along with discussion of core issues of women with AIDS. This book is not a scientific study. It is my hope that it will benefit all women and all people interested in understanding and learning how to talk to and help others who are concerned about AIDS.

AIDS will not go away. By talking about the numerous issues beyond the obvious medical factors, we are drawn closer to its victims and to each other. In this way we provide not only comfort, but hope.

1

Women's Concerns about AIDS

I wanted to find out what women would like to see in a book about women and AIDS, so I asked them. The responses varied and were worthy of a chapter. I have made an attempt to discuss these issues throughout the book.

This chapter will benefit counselors, male and female alike, who will be able to be more effective helpers after learning about women's concerns in regard to AIDS.

One of the most surprising experiences during the writing of this book was to become aware that I was "seeing" from a feminine perspective. I have always viewed AIDS as a tragedy of humankind, not specifically as a tragedy of a man or woman. It has always been difficult to differentiate the masculine/feminine aspects of my personality. I think of myself as a person rather than a woman. Although I do not consider myself a feminist, I have always felt a kinship for women and have many women friends. Through the process of writing this book I learned to focus on how to experience a feminine viewpoint.

Following are women's responses to the question, "What topics/issues would you like to see covered in a book about women and AIDS?"

Liz, Registered Nurse, San Francisco resident:

"I think that since women are probably next at risk, massive education is needed. Reality, the facts about trans-

1

mission and what happens to a person who gets AIDS, should be provided. As a nurse, I see the terrible deterioration, both physical and emotional, that AIDS people must experience. This is my AIDS education but I think the average woman doesn't see this reality.

"I would like to see more emphasis placed on honesty and fidelity in relationships. There is danger in the bisexual man who doesn't own up to his bisexuality and places his wife at risk for contracting AIDS.

"In this country in general, there is very little acceptance of bisexuality and homosexuality except in small, unique areas. Social and health responsibilities of bisexual and homosexual men should be brought into focus and not hidden from the major population. Education to discourage homophobia may help to dispel some of the fears about AIDS.

"Finally, I would like to see more focus on women in minority groups who are being more heavily affected by AIDS than the general population. I have lost several friends, all of them Latin women, to AIDS."

Several of Liz's women friends have died from AIDS-related illness, which has been devastating to all aspects of her life. She admits to being frightened and saddened but is attempting to cope by doing something to help. As a nurse she cares for AIDS patients and is attempting to bring attention to the great loss of humanity by expressing her concerns in this book.

The same question was asked of Harriet Barrett, jeweler, mother, and my friend:

"All the literature has to be out there. For each person that does read, you're reaching one more. A book about women and AIDS has to be written from the compassion end, not just from the fear end of what it is. For example: You lost your friend today—you lost your child. All these babies with AIDS are being dumped and there are so many unwanted pregnancies on top of this.

AIDS has to affect everyone right down to the economy. People say, 'Well, I live in a town where AIDS doesn't happen.' But the economy is affected because those babies that are dumped have to be taken care of. Hospitals have to deal with AIDS people. Someone's going to pay for it—we're all going to pay for it. So somehow, the people have to be reached and they have to be reached from a compassionate end, from a woman's viewpoint. Maybe not just this book, but why isn't there a women's pamphlet for women's organizations? It should cover the 'how-to's' and have AIDS articles just so it reaches more of the masses.

"I don't for one minute think I'm safe just because I'm a married woman. I don't live with that fear but it's a false thing to think that AIDS is not going to hit me and hurt me just because of my role. That's what hasn't been gotten across to all these other people who say, 'I don't hang out with gays or drug users so it's not going to happen here.' So, women, yes, that's a key thing. We are the mothers so we have to reach them.

"I think a woman's perspective is a very important place to come from. There has been such a strong networking with women. Each magazine should publish a love story that ends as a result of AIDS. The love story being about my son or my daughter. These stories should also be aimed at people who have no fear of AIDS because they are married. How about, 'Your kids are going to be sexually active tomorrow!' These people have to be hit with the facts but I wish they could be hit verbally before reality takes its toll."

Harriet, too, has lost friends to AIDS. Her insight provides constructive ways in which to reach a larger audience through magazine articles focusing on realistic love stories that involve AIDS. Harriet also stresses the far-reaching economic problems, as well as the direct personal tragedy of knowing someone who has AIDS. I too believe there is a great need to make AIDS "real" for the people who have not yet been directly affected.

Alice, mother and social worker:

"I feel it's all covered for me in my life. I know what choices I've made. But some women are in relationships with promiscuous men, which is not an uncommon thing in our society—the 'womanizing man.' It's a compulsive disorder where just being told AIDS is out there is not going to stop it. Just like an IV drug user isn't necessarily going to stop if he or she hears about AIDS.

"I would like to see. . . . I feel a very definite sisterhood with all women. I like the idea that men are a separate entity. They're impossible, you put up with them and get attracted to them. I feel strongly because I have been in relationships with womanizing men. My father's a womanizer. What must it be like to be married to someone like that? You're hooked into a relationship . . . trapped . . . can't get out, and on top of it all, there is AIDS.

"I'd like to see some help for women in these relationships, particularly. I've been in this situation myself. Help is needed not only for your self-esteem, but for your life. What would you do if you were married to one of those men and can't get out?"

Michelle T., mother and nurse:

"I strongly feel a need for education: for women, their families, their children—especially for the middle-class population. Women should know about the risks, means of transmission and prevention, and should be willing to pass this on to their peers and children.

"There is a need to try to educate women who are drug users or have partners who are drug users through social workers and social services programs. Women need to know that not only can they pass on the AIDS virus in vitro but also through breast milk. When you think of the African women who have been told not to nurse their babies, but they still do. They're still spreading it to their babies.

"I believe that a huge number of mostly heterosexual

people are passing on the AIDS virus without knowing it because they don't feel at risk—frightening.

"I received a senator's poll card in the mail recently. One of the questions on it was, 'Should AIDS testing be mandatory for marriage licenses?' I'm not a believer in random or general AIDS testing so this was a very difficult question. In the past you needed to be tested for venereal disease before getting married. I think there should be AIDS testing for marriage and pregnancy. It's very unfair to pass AIDS on to babies."

Michelle's concerns are similar to those voiced by many of the women who were interviewed for this book. The chapter on children and AIDS includes further discussion about educational concerns in the schools and from a parental aspect.

Barbara, nurse and mother:

"I would like to see safe sexual practices. The safest way . . . precautions one can take. How you can and can't get it. There are still many women who are confused and frightened about what is and is not safe."

Barbara would like to see education for women in regard to the basic facts about AIDS. She feels that many women are still confused and uneducated. See chapter 4 on heterosexual transmission for further discussion.

Patricia, social worker:

"What's going to happen to all the babies born with AIDS? Who's going to take care of them? I know these babies only generally live for a few years but in the meantime, what will happen to them?

"I remember reading an article in the summer of '87, in *Newsweek*, about a little nine-year-old girl, Celeste, and her five-year-old brother. Both had AIDS. It is believed that she is the oldest living child who was born with AIDS. She and her brother get transfusions every week at a hospital. Her brother died in November. Why is she still alive? Do children have a better survival rate than adults? Do female children have a better survival rate than male children? I would like to see some research done in this area.

"I attended an AIDS workshop and a topic of discussion was that women who have AIDS seem to die sooner than men who have AIDS. It was pointed out that women die six months to a year after onset of symptoms, while men die between six months to two and a half years after symptom onset. Why is this? Hormonal differences? We need more research in the area of male/female AIDS differences.

"I think that in the beginning, when AIDS seemed to be confined to the homosexual population, that it wasn't covered as much by the media because the 'moral majority' was using AIDS as almost a form of population control. Especially since the increased numbers of AIDS in drug users were mainly black and Hispanic. Until now, the majority of people who have died as a result of AIDS have been homosexual, black, and Hispanic drug users. Wait until AIDS hits the white, middle-class, heterosexual population. *Then* we'll really see panic and lots of research."

Patricia's concerns about the welfare of babies born with AIDS is becoming a heartbreaking reality. The mothers and fathers of these infants often die before the babies do. Social workers are becoming hard-pressed to find foster care for these babies because many people are unwilling to take them. Many foster parents are afraid of contracting the disease or fear attachment to the child who will inevitably die. This situation again points out the need for massive education. Social service agencies are in the position to be able to provide crucial fear-reducing facts and education, to people who need it most.

The next chapter relates a personal story of the death of a friend from an AIDS-related illness. Many women have experienced similar tragedies. Counselors need to be aware of the aspect of women losing friends and family members to AIDS so that they can be more effective when helping them.

2

Sebastian

As a counselor, I talk to people who have AIDS and to others that have friends, family members, or colleagues with AIDS. Before the death of Sebastian three years ago, I barely knew what AIDS was. Through the loss of a friend, a basis for understanding the tragedy of AIDS was provided. Some counselors may have yet to experience personal loss that is AIDS related. For those who have not, the following experience should be helpful in bringing the reality of loss into focus.

Bellevue Hospital, New York City, August 1985

The two hours it took to reach Bellevue Hospital from upstate New York was time enough to run through the entire gamut of emotions ending with acute anxiety. I received the phone call the night before that Sebastian was in the hospital; that he had pneumonia; that he was on a respirator, and that he had AIDS. I was told that I better get there quick if I wanted to see him before he died.

The situation seemed like a nightmare that I was hoping wouldn't be true. Sebastian was the first person I knew who had AIDS but I really couldn't believe it, not my friend. What could I say to him? This beautiful thirty-nine-year-old man was dying from a unique pneumonia because his immune system was unable to fight back due to a horrible disease that I knew nothing about.

I was warned before going in to see him that he was emaciated and on a respirator that breathed for him. Tubes were inserted through his nose and he couldn't speak. I was frightened but tried to prepare for the initial sight of Sebastian, who had always been so healthy, taking such good care of his body.

When I entered the room, I was surprised at how alert and animated Sebastian seemed. His blue eyes were sparkling and he was ready to write a note of greeting, with a pencil and paper by his side. I bent to hug him but the paraphernalia got in the way, making the hug awkward. The respirator, a breathing machine, forced oxygen through hoses into Sebastian's lungs via his mouth and throat. It made a strange whistling sound that I will never forget. Funny, because when he visited a few weeks earlier, he commented on the absence of the peepers, tiny frogs that make a wonderful peeping sound from spring to fall in the country. The several nights he stayed with us, we didn't hear them. Now, as I entered the room, I said, "Here are the peepers!" The respirator made the almost-identical sound of the tiny frogs.

I sat by Sebastian's bed and tried to converse, but every word out of my mouth seemed inane in context to the seriousness of the situation. After a few minutes, Sebastian closed his eyes and slept. Before returning to the waiting room, a nurse told me to wash my hands with disinfectant by the sink in his room. She also said to take extra precaution if I was near when mucus was suctioned from Sebastian's lungs. This was done every few hours so he wouldn't literally drown in his own body fluid that built up rapidly because of the pneumonia.

I returned to the waiting room to find several friends of mine and Sebastian's who were to be an incredible support system throughout the next two days. We were an unusual mixture of family and friends both gay and straight. We would end up taking turns sleeping in the waiting room and spending time with Sebastian. We laughed and cried together, and without these friends with which to share feelings, the ordeal would have been too great to bear.

The next time I went into Sebastian's room his temperature soared to 105 degrees. It was crucial the fever be brought down quickly so several of us rushed to get ice and alcohol to rub his body down. Several minutes after our ministrations, his fever receded and he was comfortable once again. This raging fever was to recur several times during the next two days and each time we helped reduce it. In fact, the nurses appeared relieved to have us tend to Sebastian rather than themselves.

I would like to mention that Sebastian's hospital room was not clean when I first arrived. The sheets on his bed were dirty, the trash was overfull, the floor was dirty, and the sink was clogged with debris. Sebastian had bedsores on his lower spine because he had not been turned regularly in order to prevent them. I got the distinct impression that the hospital staff was not thrilled to be around a person with AIDS, and only came to Sebastian's room when prompted to do so. When we arrived we asked that the room be cleaned while we tended to Sebastian's bedsores, turning him when he was uncomfortable and massaging him to stimulate circulation. His bedsores healed and he was more comfortable as a result.

I think we shamed the staff into doing a better job and to become less afraid of touching someone with AIDS. Most of the staff actually became devoted to Sebastian and were as devastated as we were when he died.

Sebastian's doctors were wonderful to him and to us, explaining medical procedures and how he was progressing (or should I say regressing). His health was rapidly deteriorating. His lungs were burned as a result of the hundred percent oxygen that was being pumped into them, a paradox, for the oxygen that was meant to keep him alive had damaged his lungs to the extent that they couldn't accept any more oxygen.

AIDS itself is a paradox, like the pneumonia that was ravaging Sebastian's lungs. The AIDS virus infects the specialized T cells of the immune system that function as a signal to attack when a foreign virus or bacteria invades the body. The result is the immune system literally fighting with itself against the virus that is part of the very cell that functions to signal the attack. This is why the pneumonia took its toll on Sebastian, whose immune system had nothing left to fight with.

That first night seemed bleak after Sebastian's doctor called us around to give his prognosis. He said that Sebastian's lungs were so badly damaged from the oxygen that it was a miracle he was still alive. His heart had been working under too much strain for too long, and the fluid buildup was putting an extra burden on it. The doctor said, "Tonight is crucial for Sebastian. All we can do is pray and hope for a miracle." The doctor's voice was shaky; he too let his emotions show. Somehow it allowed us the ability to lean on and help one another after the doctor exposed his own sorrow and vulnerability.

We took turns spending the night in Sebastian's room and somehow he made it through that night. At one point I remember sitting next to the bed holding Sebastian's hand, which rested on his chest, while listening to the labored beating of his heart. I thought that his heart could stop at any time. As I listened to his heavily beating heart, I felt as mortal and vulnerable as he was. It could just as easily be me lying there with hoses and tubes sprouting from my body and a heart laboring to the strange whistling sounds of the respirator. Finally I dozed.

During the night I awoke to see Sebastian's brother

standing on the opposite side of the bed, holding his other hand while he slept, tears streaming down his face. This was one of the most touching moments during the entire hospital ordeal.

Sebastian made it through the night but in the morning his heart stopped and he was gone. A few moments later he was revived by a team who performed CPR, a terrifying experience that I didn't want to see repeated. I have always had mixed feelings about bringing people back to life who have died. It depends on the situation but it seemed especially unnatural and unfair in Sebastian's case. He could only be revived to die a short time later. After this horrifying experience we asked Sebastian if he wanted to be resuscitated if his heart stopped again. He wrote, "No, only to tell you. I'll be waiting for all. I saw the white light of the cosmos. I'm at peace with myself."

I do not know what happens when a person dies, if there is an afterlife, a rebirth, etc., but I know that Sebastian saw "the white light of the cosmos," whatever that is. Somehow, his experience alleviated some of my fears about death.

The next day was a similar routine to the night before. We again took turns spending time with Sebastian. When I was with him, I broke down and started to cry. He took my hand and with an impish sparkle in his blue eyes, shook his head and smiled. He actually tried to comfort me while he was dying. His courage will remain with me always.

During this entire ordeal the most wonderful aspect was being a part of the friends who came to say good-bye. We were a constant source of support to one another and to Sebastian. I have yet to share an experience as moving as this, particularly because it was so difficult to know that we were losing a friend dear to us all. We exchanged stories and experiences revolving around Sebastian, talking about his sparkle and wonderful sense of humor. He had the ability to make each one of us feel special and loved.

At last, the morning of the final day of Sebastian's life arrived. He continued to provide support to us through humorous notes. When asked if he wanted to die, he wrote, 'No, I always loved a good party!' He was referring to the situation of all of us waiting for him to die as a party!

Sebastian remained conscious until a few hours before his death when he slipped into a coma. A few minutes after 11:00 A.M. his heart stopped and he died.

For me, Sebastian is dead only in a physical sense. I think of him often and smile remembering things we did together. I look around my house and see presents from Sebastian. When I hear the tiny frogs that peep in the spring, I think of him. When I give a workshop on AIDS, I speak of the beautiful books that he illustrated and remember him. But, I do miss being able to sit and laugh with him. I miss receiving his funny, cheerful letters and beautiful birthday cards. Sebastian will always live in my heart and mind and I miss him.

Upstate New York, a few weeks before Sebastian's death, July 1985

I would like to backtrack to a few weeks before Sebastian's death, when first suspecting he might have AIDS.

Sebastian lived in New York City and I lived in a small town in upstate New York, which is two hours north of the city. I had not seen him for several months, which was not unusual; we communicated through notes and letters when we were too busy to actually visit. He wrote and said he was coming to spend a few weeks with me and two other friends who were also friends of mine and lived nearby.

Sebastian arrived and I ran to the car to greet him. What a shock! He was emaciated and seemed as if all his spark and vitality had faded. My mouth dropped and I blurted,

"What's wrong? Are you ill?" He responded that he was just a "little depressed" because he was having difficulty with publishers and a recent book (he was an illustrator).

I thought I knew him so well that it was hard to believe he could look so poor because of problems with a book. I think that I really didn't believe him. I sensed he was covering up something much more serious, but put aside doubts at the time.

Sebastian always greeted me with a kiss, but he avoided my mouth, hugged me and pressed his cheek to mine. I thought this gesture unusual but said nothing. We went inside where I was preparing dinner for Sebastian, several friends, and my daughter. My daughter pulled me aside and said, "Mom, do you think Sebastian has AIDS?" Her question brought my doubts to the surface as I realized I had been thinking the same thoughts. I replied, "Of course not—not our friend. He is only depressed about books and publishers." Talk about denial! Everything known about AIDS at that time pointed to the likelihood that Sebastian could have it. He was a homosexual and had been sexually active, fitting right into the highest-known risk group.

To be honest, I knew very little about AIDS three years ago. I had read some magazine articles about a small number of homosexuals who were contracting this fatal disease. I thought, "How horrible," but didn't think that AIDS would affect me or anyone I knew. Later, I would unfortunately find out how wrong I was.

During dinner, Sebastian ate little if anything and had nothing to drink. This was unusual. . . . He always had a hearty appetite and loved to cook. Everyone said the meal was good so I couldn't blame his poor appetite on my cooking! He always loved a glass of wine with a nice dinner and the company of friends, but refused the wine, saying, "Maybe later." He didn't have wine later.

He spent the night and slept very late the following

morning. It was sunny and warm, a typical July day, but he sat outside bundled in hat and sweater, saying he was cold. He literally ate no breakfast or lunch and said that maybe he was catching a cold. I did not know then that the PCP (pneumocystis carinii pneumonia) that was to later cause his death was developing.

Many cues were in evidence that pointed to AIDS but I was ignorant of the subject, preferring to believe that everything was normal. Denial is a common way to avoid dealing with unpleasant issues, but eventually one finds it difficult to hide or run away indefinitely. Sooner or later reality must be confronted, which in Sebastian's case, came much too soon.

The following night he went to another friend where he was to stay a week, becoming sicker as the week elapsed. He was cold all the time (in July!) and could not seem to get warm. Finally, he felt so ill he decided to return to his doctor in New York. Upon arrival he couldn't breathe and became frightened, calling a friend who took him to the hospital. He was immediately put on a respirator. Results of blood tests and chest X rays confirmed the diagnosis of AIDS and PCP. Sebastian was dead within a week. It was over so fast that I am grateful, for otherwise he would have had a prolonged death sentence.

I need to say that the entire time Sebastian spent with me and my other friends, he did not tell us he had AIDS. He must have known. In retrospect I think that he came to say good-bye but didn't want to spoil it with AIDS conversations. After all, there was nothing that we or anyone else could do to change the diagnosis. I also think that our pity and shock would not have helped him. Right or wrong, it was his choice not to tell us. I think he felt stupid to have contracted the disease after all he knew about it and how to prevent it. With one exception, he had been celibate for a few years prior to his death because he didn't want to get AIDS. The exception was an affair with a person who later died from an AIDS-related illness. In all probability, he got it from this relationship.

So actually, Sebastian must have known after the death of his friend that his chances of having AIDS were pretty good. In all likelihood, he tested HIV positive and chose not to tell his friends. It was very brave of him not to reveal that he was sick. If I was in his place, I would fall apart, become hysterical, and tell everyone I knew. I couldn't have continued to function as well as he.

The unusual thing was that Sebastian spent time with many friends those few weeks before he died and not one of us would admit that AIDS was a possibility. We all accepted his excuse of depression, which in itself was out of character for Sebastian. We all denied reality until forced to confront it at the hospital.

The Beginning

I would like to talk about my relationship with Sebastian so that you too can appreciate the unique and special person he was.

When we first met we were art students at a school in Brooklyn. We were both twenty-one years old and lived in the same apartment building. I was married and had a two-year-old daughter. We quickly developed a warm relationship.

Sebastian was the first homosexual I knew and became friends with. Of course, many of his friends were homosexual also and I met and liked them all.

My background was of a rather sheltered and naive nature, growing up on a farm in a small rural town. There were sixty-one students in my graduating high-school class and if any were homosexuals, I certainly wasn't aware of it. At that time, homosexuality was not socially acceptable. I had heard the derogatory terms *homo* and *queer*, but they didn't affect me or anyone I knew.

Meeting Sebastian was my introduction to homosexuality. He was always very open and comfortable about who he was and made no attempts to keep the cover on it. He was a naturally happy person whose exuberance and vitality affected everyone he met in a positive way. I don't know anyone who knew him to dislike him. He was also physically attractive with fine features and sparkling blue eyes. His goodness and genuine enthusiasm, even for the simplest of things, was contagious. He had the ability to make everyone enjoy what he delighted in; for example, a particular song, painting, movie, opera, or a pretty dish.

Sebastian's talents were many, ranging from sculpting, jewelry design, fabric design, to book illustration. Everything he attempted, he did well and always shared the results of these talents with friends. All of us have a book, or a piece of jewelry he designed.

Friendship was of prime importance to Sebastian and when I moved from Brooklyn to upstate New York, he made every effort to continue our relationship. He often came for visits during holidays and wrote letters when he couldn't.

Over the nearly twenty years that spanned our relationship, Sebastian involved me in every aspect of his life. I did photographs of him for his book jackets as well as photographs that he used as models for his book illustrations. We browsed antique shops together, looking for unusual dishes and glassware.

He introduced me to opera, of which I had no previous knowledge, helping me gain understanding and love for his favorites. One night many years ago, he managed to obtain tickets to see Beverly Sills (my first opera) at the Met when neither of us really had the money for the price of seats. He made a beautiful, unusual neckpiece that fell below my waist so that I could "pretend" that I was part of the opera-going crowd—a wonderful fantasy evening that I will always remember.

An aspect of our relationship that was unique was that it was safe and comfortable. This was the first time I was able to have a close, warm relationship with a man in which sexuality wasn't the motivating factor (didn't interfere or get in the way). Sebastian wasn't interested in developing a sexual relationship with me, nor I with him. For me in the past, male friendships often deteriorated when the inevitable bottom line was sex. In particular, I remember one man I knew in college. We spent time together usually with a group of friends. One day he asked me to go out with him. I said, "We go out together all the time." He replied, "No, I mean on a date." After this interchange our relationship was never the same. I wanted a platonic friend, he wanted a sexual friend.

Sexuality is a large aspect of the human personality and it was good not to have it interfere in my relationship with Sebastian. I also think I was fortunate that my introduction to homosexuality was through Sebastian, whose outlook was open and positive, making it a good experience for me. He told me that he knew he was gay when he became an adolescent. He went through the motions of escorting girls to the various high-school proms, but was never physically attracted to them. He did it more for the sake of conventionality. Homosexuality was not socially acceptable when he was a teenager in the late 1950s. When he finally went to college he could openly express gender preference without the fear of ridicule.

Sebastian was childlike, not in a naive way, but in his ability to take genuine delight in simple pleasures, seeing through a child's eyes the beauty and wonder that most of us unfortunately lose as we become adults. Most of all, I loved him for his ability to impart this to me. We had so much fun. Sebastian, I miss you.

Many women have had and will have experiences similar to this one. Further discussion about the biological and psychological aspects of AIDS in relation to women is presented in the following chapter. Counselors need to understand the physical and emotional characteristics of AIDS so that they may distinguish between untruths and real underlying concerns that women will present.

3

What Is AIDS?—A Primer for Women

Many counselors will be approached for information about the biological aspects of AIDS. While these requests can be referred to the many hot-line numbers, the curiosity about AIDS is often an ongoing one that occurs again and again. School psychologists will be asked to explain AIDS to teachers; nursing assistants will have many questions for nurses; families in counseling will wonder about an acquaintance or colleague and will turn to the family therapist. In all the cases, it is helpful for counselors to be conversant with the biological bases of AIDS in order to be able to answer some of these questions directly, or to know when a request for information is really a statement of an underlying concern.

Part 1: Biological Aspects

AIDS, an acronym for aquired immune deficiency syndrome, is a condition caused by a retrovirus that attacks the major cells of the immune system in the human body. The immune system literally fights against itself leaving the body open to a variety of opportunistic infections and malignancies that in turn are the cause of death. AIDS is an ultimately fatal disease and at this time there is no cure.

Aside from the destruction of the immune system the

AIDS virus also attacks brain cells, having no problem getting through the blood brain barrier, so in effect the brain acts as a sanctuary for the virus. Many drugs that may be used to treat disease in the brain cannot get through the blood brain barrier. Results of AIDS viral brain invasion are dementia, loss of memory, irreparable brain tissue damage, i.e., shriveled cerebral cortex, and enlarged ventricles.

Research has identified a virus that is linked to AIDS, but as yet there is no conclusive proof that this virus is the sole cause of AIDS. In the United States this virus is called HTLV-111 (human T-cell lymphotropic virus, type III) while in France, it is called LAV (lymphadenopathy-associated virus).

The virus will be called HIV (human immunodeficiency virus) an internationally accepted, shortened term, for purposes of this book.

There has been a great deal of evidence that cofactors, in addition to the presence of the HIV virus itself, may be necessary to trigger the onset of full-blown AIDS. Possible cofactors may be general health of the person, poor sanitation, prescribed and recreational drugs, malnutrition, and infections, including other sexually transmitted diseases. However, no particular cofactor has been directly linked to the onset of AIDS.

Transmission Modes

AIDS is a sexually transmitted disease that must get into the actual body plasma (blood) to become active. HIV can also be spread intravenously, through the sharing of contaminated needles among IV drug users or through a blood transfusion. All blood in the US has been screened for HIV since April of 1985. It is still theoretically possible to get AIDS from a transfusion, although highly unlikely. Because of the long incubation period, HIV-infected donated blood could get through the screening procedure, not yet having produced AIDS antibodies that can be detected.

It takes direct blood-to- blood or semen-to-blood contact to transmit the virus. Although the virus has been isolated in small amounts in some AIDS-infected individuals' body fluids, i.e., saliva, tears, there is no evidence that the virus can be transmitted by these fluids.

The AIDS virus can be transmitted neonatally through an HIV-infected mother to the fetus or to an infant via its mother's milk.

AIDS is not discriminatory; anyone can get it, but it is not easy to transmit. It cannot be spread via the air, food, water, environmental surfaces, or casual contact with an AIDS-infected person. No one can get AIDS from living, working, or going to school with someone who has AIDS.

The AIDS virus is fragile, only existing outside of the body for a few minutes. It can be destroyed by common household bleach or heat (sterilization).

Risk Groups

Presently in the United States, there are several risk groups: homosexual men, IV drug users, sex partners (male and female) of persons infected with HIV, and newborn infants of women infected with HIV. Transfusion recipients and hemophiliacs, who received donated blood or blood products prior to April 1985 are also at risk.

To date, the two largest risk groups in the United States are homosexual men and IV drug users. These groups seem to have provided the disease an easy means of transmission via contaminated needle sharing and body fluid exchange through anal intercourse. Anal intercourse between men appears to be the highest-risk sexual activity because of the likelihood of tears in the mucous membrane of the colon and rectum, allowing the virus direct access into the bloodstream.

Vaginal transmission of the virus has been established and is becoming a growing concern in the United States. In Africa, the main spread of AIDS occurs through heterosexual transmission. For further discussion, see the following chapter on heterosexual transmission.

Demographics/Statistics

It is estimated, through the WHO (World Health Organization), that there are ten million people infected with HIV worldwide. Between one to two million of these infected people are located in central Africa. To date, at least fifty thousand Africans, both men and women, have contracted AIDS since 1980.

In the United States there is a reported figure upward of twenty-one thousand AIDS cases, with an estimated five hundred thousand to one million carriers. These carriers are generally symptomless and could be spreading the disease unknowingly. One-third of the twenty-one thousand HIV-infected people are in New York City, where AIDS is the leading cause of death of men and women between the ages of twenty and forty. Within the next five years, AIDS is expected to kill another twenty-five thousand Americans.

The virus's incubation period can be anywhere between six months and seven years (some researchers say it can be upward of ten years!) depending on the method of transmission.

The presence of HIV can be detected by the ELISA (Enzyme-Linked Immunosorbent Assay) test that reacts to HIV antibodies in the blood. If the test is positive for HIV, a more specific and expensive test can be performed—the Western Blot—before a person is definitely considered to have been infected with the AIDS virus. Even with a positive test result, it is not known who will go on to develop AIDS. Positive test results can mean one of four of the following: (1) false positive—found often in women who had previous pregnancy; test reacted to something else in the blood, (2) the body has met with the AIDS virus and has successfully fought it off, (3) the person has live AIDS virus in the blood but is not sick (no symptoms), (4) the person has been infected with HIV and will develop AIDS. All of the above must be considered potentially infective for an indefinite period.

The most common symptoms (accompanied by no other known illness) of AIDS include fever over a hundred degrees, night sweats (more than two months), loss of appetite, weight loss of ten pounds or more, fatigue, swollen glands, shortness of breath, persistent diarrhea, creamy white patches on inside of mouth (thrush), and purplish-bluish raised or flat patches occurring first on outer extremities (Kaposis' sarcoma). Some people who become infected with HIV have many of the symptoms listed above but to a lesser degree; this condition is usually referred to as ARC (AIDS-related complex). It is estimated that 30 percent of these people will go on to develop full-blown AIDS.

Pediatric AIDS (PAIDS) occurs in children under thirteen years of age; it is transmitted neonatally through mother to fetus. Most infants are born with it from an infected mother and fail to thrive. HIV is also found in breast milk. It is rare for these children to live to school age. Hemophiliac children have also become infected through contaminated blood products prior to April 1985. Unfortunately, the number of babies born with AIDS is on the upswing. A recent study showed one in sixty-one babies born in New York City was infected with HIV.

Etiology

The origin of the AIDS virus is believed to be Central Africa although this has not been proven through research. The virus has been isolated in the African green monkey that acts as host and carrier.

HIV is a fragile virus that can only exist outside the body for a short period of time. It must live within a cell to be active or functional. HIV does not survive on environmental surfaces, personal objects, or eating utensils.

HIV is a retrovirus that is characterized by the capability via an enzyme, "reverse transcriptase," of encoding on DNA in the human body. DNA, in turn, has the genetic code or makeup of the virus that is replicated when the cell divides. The virus only damages but does not kill the infected T cell that it has an affinity for.

The Immune System: A Closer Look

The immune system is a complex network of specialized cells and organs that defend the body against foreign invaders. When it malfunctions, it leaves the body open to a variety of diseases ranging from allergies to cancer.

Characteristics of the immune system are the ability to distinguish between "self" and "nonself" molecules; it has a memory; for example, once a person has the mumps he or she won't get it again; and it is both specific and diversified, having the ability to recognize many millions of nonself molecules and can produce molecules to match and counteract each nonself molecule.

Antigens are nonself molecules that may trigger a response in the immune system; they can be a virus, bacteria, fungus, or parasite. Proteins can be rejected if they are not first broken down into building blocks by the digestive system. Tissues from other individuals can also be rejected, e.g., organ transplant recipients—the normal body response is to reject this foreign tissue. These people must be put on immunosuppressant drugs to counteract organ rejection.

In abnormal situations the immune system can identify "self" as "nonself," resulting in autoimmune diseases such as rheumatoid arthritis. In certain people harmless substances such as cat hair or ragweed pollen can provoke the immune system to set off the inappropriate response known as "allergy." In these cases, the antigens are known as allergens.

The organs of the immune system are referred to as lymphoid organs because they are concerned with growth, development, and deployment of lymphocytes, which are the white blood cells that are the key operators of the immune system. The lymphoid organs are bone marrow—where lymphocytes are produced (specifically B cells); thymus—the gland under the breastbone where the T cells mature; lymph nodes—in groin, neck, abdomen, and armpits where the lymphatic vessels carry lymph that contains lymphocytes cycled throughout the body on patrol of foreign invasion; spleen—B cell lymphocytes spend time in the spleen during their cycle. If there is spleen trauma, the body is open to infection.

The cells of the immune system are called lymphocytes, which are white cells that carry out the activation of the immune system. The B cell lymphocytes are processed outside the thymus and secrete antibodies that exactly match specific invading antigens. This key-and-lock system can sometimes inactivate antigens but it is not effective against intracellular viruses, i.e., HIV.

The two types of T cell lymphocytes are T4 (helper) cells and T8 (killer) cells. T4 (helper) cells guide and turn on antibody production. The AIDS virus has an affinity for the T4 cell. T8 (killer) cells—whose key role is immune surveillance—go into action from prior stimulation of specific antigens.

Allergies are disorders of the immune system, i.e., hives, asthma, hay fever, that are a result of the immune system responding to a false alarm. Immune deficiency disease is another disorder in which one or more components of the immune system is lacking. It can be inherited such as in severe combined immune deficiency disorder (SCID) in which individuals ("bubble kids") need to live in a germ-free environment to survive. Immune deficiency disease can also be aquired through illness, side effects of drugs, or the result of stress, which depresses the T4 helper cells.

Opportunistic Infections and Malignancies Common to People with AIDS

People do not die from AIDS: it is the opportunistic infections and cancers that are the cause of death. The AIDS symptoms listed earlier in this chapter are a syndrome of various diseases and infections that people with functioning immune systems do not usually get. Following is a list of the more common diseases resulting from an AIDS-crippled immune system.

Pneumocystis Carinii Pneumonia (PCP): PCP is a parasitic (protozoan) lung infection that includes symptoms of any other type of pneumonia: dry cough, high fevers, and shortness of breath. Although the PCP protozoan is a common organism present in most people, it usually only affects people with impaired immune systems. Approximately 60 percent of AIDS patients get it; 50 percent die of it and it can be recurring. PCP is diagnosed by a procedure called a bronchoscopy, in which the doctor inserts a long tube into the lungs, performing both a biopsy and visual examination.

Candida or thrush: a fungal infection, manifesting itself as a whitish coating inside the mouth on the tongue and throat. Thrush is usually not life-threatening and can be treated with antifungal tablets to keep it in check.

Herpes simplex: a virus found in most people with AIDS that can cause varying problems including pain and fever. Painful sores can be present on the lips, mouth, and genital areas. Herpes can be treated with topical cream (Zovirax) or with an oral or intravenous drug called acyclovir. Common to people with AIDS—take precaution because herpes is contagious, i.e., no kissing.

Herpes Zoster: a viral form of chicken pox commonly called *shingles* present in nerve cells; manifests itself as an infection appearing as raised, red bumps on the skin that can turn into painful, itching sores accompanied by fever. Treatment is the same (acyclovir) as for herpes simplex.

Cytomegalovirus (CMV): a common viral infection in people with AIDS that can infect various organs, i.e., eyes, liver, lungs, brain, colon. If untreated, CMV can cause chronic diarrhea, wasting, and blindness. An experimental drug, DHPG, can be used to keep the virus in check.

A word of caution to pregnant women who may be nurses or health-care workers working with AIDS patients. CMV is contagious; a pregnant woman can become infected with CMV causing organ damage to her unborn fetus. Precaution should be taken to avoid infection.

Toxoplasmosis: a parasitic infection, "toxo," that invades the nervous system and brain, causing seizures, high fevers, loss of consciousness, and loss of sensation in arms or legs. Toxo is treated with drug therapy, i.e., sulfadiazine.

Cryptococcal meningitis: a yeast infection that manifests itself as brain inflammation (meningitis) causing severe headaches, high fevers, swollen glands, and endocarditis (inflammation surrounding the heart). Treatment of the drug amphotericin B, can bring it under control, but not get rid of it.

Leukoencephalopathy: a slowly progressive dementia that is incapacitating and eventually fatal. Its symptoms begin with fevers, loss of memory and motor control, delusions, hallucinations, and headaches. At this time, leukoencephalopathy is not treatable.

Kaposi's Sarcoma (KS): a cancer of the small blood vessels, usually first appearing as red blotches on the skin that become purplish, raised lesions. They often appear on the limbs, chest, neck, back, and face, eventually compromising internal organs, i.e., lungs, colon, intestines. KS is a common opportunistic cancer that infects AIDS patients, causing death about twenty-five percent of the time. Radiation and chemotherapy can be somewhat effective in treatment.

This unusual form of cancer was only found previously in middle-aged European-Mediterranean males with a mean age of sixty-three or in some immunosupressed African children. Prior to the AIDS outbreak, KS had been found in a small number of kidney transplant recipients in the United States.

Lymphomas: cancer of the lymph nodes occurring in many people with AIDS that rapidly spreads to bone marrow and the central nervous system. Does not respond well to chemotherapy, which allows for the onset of other opportunistic infections.

Treatment

Research has yet to find a cure for AIDS. Development of a vaccine is hindered by the variability of the virus within and between people infected by it, but more is being learned about HIV from experimental studies resulting in hope toward discovery of a cure.

Experimental treatments for AIDS consist of reconstitution and enhancement of the immune system through bone marrow transplants and transfusions, and antiviral immunology using vaccine. The rationale behind antiviral vaccines is to inhibit the enzyme "reverse transcriptase," rendering it ineffective to encode HIV into the DNA of a cell.

Some HIV-infected children and adults receive immune-system enhancement and reconstitution treatments every few weeks. Apparently, these experimental treatments are somewhat effective, depending on the stage of disease in helping prolong life through suppression of the virus.

Certain experimental drugs, such as AZT, also appear effective in suppressing the virus in some individuals, but do not make the HIV disappear. Again, the effectiveness of the drug depends on the particular individual's reaction to it and the state of the disease. AZT has enhanced the quality of life and helped to prolong it in some people with AIDS.

Prevention/Precautions

It is known how AIDS is transmitted; therefore, it is known how not to get it. For those fortunate enough not to have AIDS at this time, there are many precautions that may be taken. Following are concerns of particular interest to women.

* * *

Since AIDS is a sexually transmitted disease, the first and most obvious means of avoiding it is to take sexual precautions by following "safer sex" guidelines, particularly if one is not in a monogamous relationship. Limit your sex partners, preferably to one person who has done the same. Before becoming involved with someone new, it is important to find out your future partner's health status and whether or not he or she has had other sex partners. The bottom line may be testing for both of you to make sure neither has been exposed to HIV.

If you are unsure of your partner's sexual history, do not exchange blood or semen. During sexual intercourse, always use condoms with a spermicide (Nonoxynol-9), which decreases risk of infection if used properly. (A word of warning here. . . . condoms do not guarantee the prevention of AIDS; if uncertain of your partner's AIDS status, abstain from sex until you are certain. We are talking life and death!) See the following chapter on heterosexual transmission for a more detailed discussion.

A second important precaution is to attempt to maintain a healthy and strong immune system by eating well, avoiding heavy use of tobacco and alcohol, avoiding recreational/illicit drugs, getting enough rest and exercise.

Third, do not share certain personal items that may be contaminated with blood such as toothbrushes or razors. As mentioned before, the AIDS virus dies soon after being exposed outside of the body, but it is common sense not to share objects that may have come into recent contact with blood. It is also a good idea to ensure that your dentist takes proper precaution against HIV contaminants by wearing gloves and a mask while working on patients.

Another preventive measure to decrease the spread of AIDS is not to donate blood, body organs, or sperm if you are in a high-risk group or test positive for the AIDS antibodies.

Finally, it is imperative that AIDS education be provided in schools and to the general public. In regard to AIDS, ignorance is not bliss! Massive education is imperative. This topic will be discussed further in the chapter, "Children and AIDS."

Part 2: Psychological/Emotional Aspects

AIDS is a disease with potentially devastating psychological consequences. Seventy percent of all people diagnosed with AIDS die within two years. To date, ninety percent of all people with AIDS are relatively young, between the ages of twenty and forty-nine, an age at which people are not psychologically prepared to die. This fact is in itself, a terrible tragedy. Few other diseases produce such devastation: loss of physical and mental ability, self-sufficiency, ability to work, material necessities of income and housing, self-esteem, and emotional support of family and friends. The frightening episodes of life-threatening opportunistic infections further weaken the patient's ability to cope with psychological stress. It is helpful for psychologists, social workers, and other therapists to have an overview of these issues to allow them to be more empathetic.

The Range of Emotional Suffering

Infection with HIV causes extreme distress for most women who have been diagnosed with AIDS. The onset of symptoms, which include weight loss, persistent infections, general malaise, and swollen lymph glands, is typically accompanied by fear of developing AIDS. The diagnosis itself can bring relief to some who have anticipated the disease with anxiety and dread.

Anxiety and depression are the most common psychological factors related to the illness. Preoccupation with imminent death is revealed in distress or anxiety, similar to people with certain cancers and other terminal diseases. At the time of diagnosis, a woman may feel disbelief and outright inability to accept the fact that she has the disease. She may be angry at the disease, at the discrimination and prejudice that accompanies it, at the medical staff and profession, at the prospect of a lonely, painful death, and at herself. Those who view themselves as innocent victims are particularly prone to anger. It is not uncommon for a woman to develop guilt about past behaviors such as drug abuse or a particular life-style that may have been conducive to the development of the disease. Guilt may also be associated with the possibility of having given the disease to others. Hopelessness, withdrawal, isolation, helplessness, and other symptoms of depression are often present. Many women contemplate suicide, resulting from the anticipation of a painful death, although few actually attempt it.

For women with AIDS, a strong network of family and friends is important in providing both psychological and physical support. A drug abuser may be estranged from her family, creating additional strain when the family finds out.

A woman with AIDS may be prone to anxiety evidenced by agitation, rapid heartbeat, extreme tension, insomnia, and panic attacks.

It is common for a woman to employ the defense mechanism of denial, a psychological term, which keeps her from realizing the reality of her situation because it is too stressful to bear. She may alternate between hypersensitivity about the disease to realistic concern. A woman with AIDS may tend to see any new physical symptom as a step nearer to death.

The emotional difficulties a woman with AIDS must face present a bleak psychological picture, but there is help for those who seek it. Many forms of assistance are available aside from medical care. Referrals to local AIDS service groups are accessible. A social worker can help plan for financial and physical assistance. Psychotheraputic support is available. See the appendix for a listing of statewide resources and AIDS hot-line phone numbers.

Motherhood

The core issues of women with AIDS differ from those of men in that women do not face the stigma of contracting and transmitting the disease through homosexuality, and women can have children. Motherhood is the unique difference between men and women when AIDS is involved.

Pregnant women infected with the AIDS virus have a greater than fifty percent chance of passing it to their newborn. Unfortunately, in the United States, the number of AIDS-infected babies is rising dramatically.

A recent New York State study on AIDS and newborns produced shocking statistics: one in every sixty-one babies born in New York City, in February 1988, tested positive to HIV antibodies, indicating that the mothers were infected and that many of the infants were AIDS carriers. It is more than likely that many of these AIDS-infected mothers were or have been drug users or had sexual partners with AIDS. Many women remain ignorant about how the disease is transmitted and how to prevent it. Stronger efforts are being made to reach the uneducated, but it's too late for the babies who are born infected with AIDS. The tragedy is that women of childbearing age are those most likely to become infected.

In relation to motherhood, this woman has a disappointing story to share. Jan is a twenty-eight-year-old nurse who was recently married. She and her husband were planning to have their first child this year. One of Jan's hospital patients has AIDS. When drawing blood from this particular patient, Jan accidently stuck her hand with the needle she was using to draw blood. She waited a few weeks then had a blood test for the presence of AIDS antibodies. Although the test results were negative, she must wait a few months before being retested, to make certain she was not infected with the virus. Jan says that she doesn't think her chances of testing positive for the AIDS virus is likely to happen, but she and her husband are sad that they must put pregnancy on hold for several months.

Although Jan is disappointed in having to wait for a child, she is taking a responsible and necessary step to ensure that she will not give birth to a baby who may become infected with the AIDS virus. Awareness of precautionary measures to protect an unborn child from the disease is crucial to the future of our children. AIDS education for young women who will have children can result in AIDS-free births.

Counselors and helpers need to be aware of the heartbreak that involves women and their children. Here is a story from the *San Francisco Chronicle* (November 9, 1987) about a woman that everyone can learn from. She can give everyone a lesson in compassion and courage.

Mary B., thirty-nine-year-old nurse and mother, accidently plunged the entire contents of a syringe of AIDS-infected blood into her thigh while drawing the blood from a patient. Two weeks later, Mary tested positive for AIDS antibodies. Four weeks after testing, she developed one of the symptoms of AIDS, an opportunistic infection called thrush (candida albicans).

The most difficult aspect was for Mary to find a way to tell her twelve-year-old daughter that she had the disease. She didn't want her daughter to feel ashamed that she had AIDS. Mary wasn't ashamed because she got AIDS by helping someone. On the other hand, she had to explain that her daughter shouldn't talk about it in school because of the possibility of community hysteria.

Mary's personal life wasn't the same after she contracted AIDS. "Except for one or two people, I've had to develop a whole new set of friends, a network of people who are involved with AIDS," she said. "It seems so drastic and unnecessary but that's the reality of what I've had to do."

Mary doesn't hold any grudges against the friends that deserted her or even against the patient and the hospital where she contracted the disease. "I'd hug that patient who gave it to me if I could," she said. She would do it all again if called on to help.

Looking to the future, Mary is not frightened because she has AIDS. "It's almost a bit of a gift knowing so soon after the accident that you actually have the disease because it gives you time to plan what you want to do with the rest of your life. So now I have a whole different perspective on life, and I can do all the things that ought to be done. I can fight to make people understand the disease so they'll accept the people who have it."

Today, Mary has helped organize Sacramento's first support group for women who have AIDS. She has taken charge of her life through AZT treatments and continues to hold a positive, optimistic outlook. Mary's strength and courage can be a model for all of us. I find it rewarding to hear a courageous story such as this that provides a glimmer of hope in this time of tragedy and AIDS. Many times counselors learn from their clients. For therapists working with AIDS issues, there may be areas of stress and burnout, but also stories of courage and of the incredible resiliency of the human spirit against indomitable odds, as these vignettes have shown.

The following chapter discusses the heterosexual transmission mode of AIDS as well as the concerns and fears of women in relationship to it.

4

Women's Concerns about Heterosexual Transmission

People are being bombarded with a plethora of mixed messages in regard to the heterosexual transmission of AIDS. The Centers for Disease Control estimate that thirty thousand heterosexuals, not displaying other risk factors, are carrying the AIDS virus. Masters and Johnson estimate this figure to be as high as two hundred thousand. Who is to be believed?

Research has proven that AIDS is a sexually transmitted disease that can be given to a female by a HIV-infected male, and vice versa. Anal sex is the highest-risk sexual practice because of the likelihood of a tear occurring in the rectal mucous membrane, allowing easy HIV entrance into the body. Therefore, a woman would be at the receptive end of anal sex, and at greater risk of contracting the virus if her partner is infected.

The *Science Times* section of the *New York Times*, Tuesday, March 22, 1988, provided a closer look at new findings of the strategy of the AIDS virus. Researchers say they have a much clearer picture of how the virus enters and invades the body. The virus has been found to infect both the cervix and the cells of the rectum and colon. These findings suggest that infection may occur by *direct viral contact* of the virus with the rectum and female genitalia. This would explain the recent increase of AIDS in heterosexuals, and the apparent easy HIV spread to babies born of infected mothers.

A pregnant woman whose cervix is infected with the AIDS virus could easily transmit the HIV to her baby during the birth process. As the baby travels down the birth canal, it would come into direct contact with the HIV-infected cervix, thus increasing the chances of infection.

This study, published in the March 1988 issue of the *Annals of Internal Medicine,* used tissue samples of four HIV-infected women. The women were heroin users, assumed to be infected by the use of contaminated needles. Researchers suggest that the virus spread from the blood to the cervix via the bloodstream. These findings certainly widen the possibility of an easy, direct mode of heterosexual HIV transmission.

The *Journal of the American Medical Association* published a recent article (April 22, 1988) that lists the odds of getting AIDS through heterosexual intercourse. Research was conducted on heterosexuals of various backgrounds to provide statistics on the likelihood of contracting the disease, according to numbers of sexual encounters and the risk category of the sexual partner.

The major finding of the study is that the degree of risk is determined largely by whether one's sexual partner is from a high-risk group for contracting AIDS, i.e., IV drug user, bisexual male, blood transfusion recipient before 1985, hemophiliac.

The researchers recommend that heterosexuals protect themselves from AIDS by only having sexual contact with low-risk partners. This recommendation varies widely from previous advice that has emphasized other protective measures: reducing the number of sexual partners, using condoms, avoiding anal sex, or asking one's sexual partner to pass an AIDS test.

This analysis states that the chance of contracting AIDS through a single act of heterosexual intercourse with a low-risk partner is one in five million, if a condom is used and the partner has tested negative for the virus.

The risk for the same single sex act with a high-risk partner increases to one in five hundred, if the partner is HIV-infected and no condom is used.

By comparison, the odds of winning the current Lotto game sponsored by the New York State Lottery are one in thirteen million.

The researchers warn that although the estimates are generally statistically sound, there may be wide variation among individuals in regard to their chances of transmitting or contracting the virus.

New York City commissioner of health, Dr. Stephen C. Joseph, agrees that the research is basically accurate, but he would treat the statistics as very tentative. He agrees that the individual risk of contracting AIDS from a single heterosexual encounter with an infected partner is very small. Dr. Joseph says that this statistic may help to reassure the person who had a single high-risk encounter several years ago, and is still worrying about it.

AIDS epidemiologist at the Federal Centers for Disease Control, Dr. Harold Jaffe, also agrees with the report's estimates, but cautions people to continue other safe sexual practices, as well. He suggests condom use, knowing your partner, and the avoidance of anal sex.

Because of the large homosexual incidence of AIDS, research has focused on homosexual males and has practically avoided women. According to Dr. Matilde Krim, AZT is the only FDA-approved drug that is currently used to fight AIDS. AZT was never tested on women, although it is now prescribed for them. Dr. Krim says, "Clinical trials for AIDS have been so few, that investigators have chosen the most controlled conditions possible. Working exclusively with gay men accomplishes this because they are homogeneous in risk factors. Women are being excluded because of the assumption by doctors, that they are IV drug users and therefore, undesirable patients."

The Centers for Disease Control give yet another message. They say fewer than half the AIDS-infected women are current or former drug users. That leaves an estimated two thousand women, in the United States, who have contracted the disease through other avenues (*Village Voice*, February 16, 1988). Unfortunately, discrimination exists for women in regard to AIDS clinical/drug trials.

It's possible that Masters and Johnson, as a result of their new book, will reverse the bias that exists in research toward women in regard to clinical trials. In their new book, *Crisis: Heterosexual Behavior in the Age of AIDS*, Masters, Johnson, and Kolodny conducted a study on eight hundred heterosexuals between the ages of twenty-one and forty. Four hundred of the subjects were monogamous, and the other four hundred were considered promiscuous, having had at least six sexual relationships with different partners in the course of a year.

The findings were as follows: of the four hundred monogamous people, one was found to be infected with HIV; of the four hundred who had multiple sexual partners, 7 percent of the women and 5 percent of the men tested HIV positive. All of the subjects were supposedly not part of any other risk group. The results of this study may be difficult to extrapolate to the entire heterosexual population in the United States.

Masters, Johnson, and Kolodny were criticized by national medical and health organizations for their research methods. An improperly controlled study that resulted in invalid findings is the accusation.

In their defense, the authors argue that the Centers for Disease Control have not conducted any wide-scale studies on heterosexual incidence of AIDS. Studies are only being conducted on heterosexuals in conjunction with drug abuse.

Masters, Johnson, and Kolodny believe that AIDS has infected many more heterosexuals than the CDC estimate. Based on their research, they warn that heterosexuals should be much more concerned about AIDS than is currently the situation.

Whether or not the authors' predictions are entirely accurate, I believe that the estimates and implications should be taken seriously. I can only guess at the heterosexual prevalence of AIDS in the United States, but one thing is certain; AIDS is transmitted sexually, and heterosexuals can get and do get AIDS. I tend to think that people in the United States forget that the incidence of AIDS in certain central African countries, for example, resides almost entirely in the heterosexual population, with a balance of 50 percent male, 50 percent female. These countries have an estimated incidence of AIDS that suggests that more than one-third of the entire population is infected with the virus. This estimate focuses on urban areas, but nevertheless is a staggering figure. I have heard predictions that within ten years, 90 percent of the entire population in these high-AIDS-incidence countries will be dead, unless a cure is found.

It seems more than likely, that if the majority of the heterosexuals in the United States do not feel at any great risk for getting AIDS, then they will take fewer precautions to avoid spreading it. This lack of concern may result in the HIV inroad into the heterosexual population.

An even more worrisome avenue of heterosexual transmission is through adolescents. Despite the fact that there has been a gush of television promotion of AIDS awareness, many kids are not getting the gist of what they are being bombarded with. Among the women interviewed for this book who have children, there is a consensus that media advertising on AIDS is going over the kids' heads.

Many children, particularly preadolescents, do not know what a condom is. Condom messages are being inserted between Saturday morning cartoons and children's shows. Children have to rely on their parents for information to clarify television AIDS messages. Many parents were not aware that their kids were not understanding the content of AIDS media advertising.

For example, Harriet Barrett tells of the lack of understanding revealed by her eleven-year-old daughter and fourteen-year-old son:

"I asked my daughter what she knew about AIDS. She said, 'You get it through sexual intercourse. What's that?' I think that the AIDS messages are on television so often, that it becomes nonreal. I didn't realize that until I approached the kids, who listen to this advertising about condoms, etc.

"I approached my son about working with a friend of ours who has AIDS, and I wanted to be straightforward, so I asked him what he knew about AIDS. He said, 'I don't know.' It is just another cartoon to him. I don't know if he wasn't capable of approaching me because I'm his mother, or in fact, he really doesn't know what he's seeing on TV, which I suspect is the case. The media messages are not reaching him.

"Unfortunately, talking AIDS with children has to be much more of a one-to-one thing."

Harriet's viewpoint is one that other mothers share. I believe that even if kids are understanding the AIDS messages, there is another factor that interferes with taking AIDS seriously. Most teens feel invulnerable. I remember my teen years, and how it was much easier to do things without the worry of consequences. This is the nature of the adolescent; the hormones. You are young, your life is ahead of you, you don't have the worries of an adult. You are beginning to make choices on your own. Death and AIDS are not in the scheme of things.

The adolescents I've talked to have all heard of AIDS, but my fear for these kids is that their lack of involvement with the reality of the disease may lead to risk-taking behaviors. I am sure that there are many young people who engage in sex without using condoms, and experiment with drugs without taking consequences into consideration. This is dangerous behavior that can result in AIDS infection.

Adolescents at the most risk for contracting AIDS are the street kids who have run away from home. Misinformation and the more immediate problems of shelter and food make it difficult for these kids to worry about the future and the possibility of getting AIDS.

A recent article in the January 1988 issue of *Psychology Today* takes a close look at AIDS and the runaway in conjunction with Covenant House, New York City's largest shelter for runaway children. The article stated that teenagers are being used for sexual recreation by men; in cars, subway stations, bus stations, hotels, alleys, and right on the streets. Why are the customers who purchase sex not afraid of getting AIDS? Denial is a factor, and men who buy sex want fantasy rather than the reality of condoms and precautions that may prevent the contraction of AIDS.

Most runaways are not teenage adventurers. They are scared kids trying to avoid the stressful, dysfunctional home environment that fosters physical and sexual abuse. Sex is often the only road to survival for these kids, and it's sex that puts them in great jeopardy of contracting and spreading AIDS. Prostitution is the norm, but even the few who don't sell sex to survive, more than likely have sex with drug-abusing boyfriends.

Urban areas hold the greatest AIDS risk for homeless kids. They have more exposure to drugs and sexually transmitted disease. Often, their immune systems have already been compromised by repeated exposure to infections that may increase the risk of getting AIDS. These kids feel invulnerable and don't think beyond today.

This particular population is probably the most difficult to educate because it is transient, and physically difficult to reach. Covenant House attempts the extremely difficult, but necessary, task of trying to help runaways by providing food, shelter, medical assistance, condoms, and AIDS education.

I doubt that in the near future, the mode of AIDS transmission through adolescents will be closed. Bravo to Covenant House for the continuing efforts to reach these children.

Prostitution is another serious threat to the heterosexual transmission of AIDS. A Centers for Disease Control study of 2,059 AIDS patients who appeared to be infected from unknown sources were examined. Nine hundred and twenty-one subjects were excluded from the study because of unavailable medical histories. Thirty-two subjects were incorrectly diagnosed as having AIDS. Seventy-two percent of the remaining cases were involved with high-risk behavior, not initially reported. Of the two-thirds of the remaining cases, 38 percent had visited prostitutes (*New York Times*, March 4, 1988).

I don't think prostitutes are being considered as much of a threat in the spread of AIDS, and I wonder why. Studies conducted in several cities in the United States involving prostitutes, tested for the presence of HIV antibodies, have revealed startling statistics. Following is a list of the prevalence of AIDS in 568 United States female prostitutes who participated in the 1987 study that was published in *Morbidity and Morality Weekly Report*, 36:157. Those who tested positive for HIV are reflected in the percentages:

(1) Newark/Jersey City/ Paterson—57.1 percent
(2) Miami—18.7 percent
(3) San Francisco—6.2 percent
(4) Los Angeles—4.3 percent
(5) Colorado Springs—1.4 percent
(6) Atlanta—1 percent
(7) Las Vegas—0.0 percent

A survey in Newark reported that half of seventy-eight streetwalkers tested positive for the AIDS virus (*New York Times*, December 21, 1987). An interview with one of the streetwalkers, a twenty-six-year-old, reveals her attitudes toward AIDS. She says, "I have two little girls to support. It's just for the money. I use condoms; I've got one right here. I used several today. I'm out here a couple of hours already." She says that most of her business is oral sex; usually white men from the suburbs, who ask her into their cars. She explains that a "trick" is over in three to five minutes, and it costs twenty dollars.

She describes how to put a condom on a "john" (customer) without his knowing it. "Most girls don't use condoms," she said. "A lot of girls if I ask them for one when I run out, they never have one."

AIDS isn't something she worries about. "You can just as easy get it at home or on the streets—just kissing your boyfriend. I don't know who he could be doing it with. There's no one-woman men or one-man women anymore. The johns could be bringing AIDS home to their wives."

When asked what she does with her money, she replied,

"You can't stay nowhere for free." She also has a sixty-dollar-a-day heroin habit.

She said she tested negative for the AIDS virus. "Girls that test positive still work. They've gotta make a living. The tricks ask me if I have AIDS. I say, 'Does it look like I have AIDS?' They ask but they don't be serious. If they really care, they won't be asking."

Shortly after this interview, Newark passed an ordinance in regard to prostitutes and their customers. If arrested and convicted, they must submit to AIDS antibody tests. If the convicted person refuses to submit to testing, he or she can be fined up to one thousand dollars, and put in jail for ninety days (*New York Times*, January 6, 1988).

Nevada, Illinois, and Florida also have laws under which prostitutes may be required to submit to AIDS antibody testing.

In Salt Lake City, I interviewed a young, homeless streetwalker about her concerns about AIDS. This beautiful girl stays with a group of homeless people. She said that she knows about AIDS, but doesn't always use condoms. "Some of my tricks don't go for condoms, so I don't use them all the time. I wouldn't make any money if I did. A lot of guys like it without."

She hasn't been tested for HIV antibodies. "I feel good, so why bother? I don't have the time." She is having sex with one of the homeless men she stays with. She says she loves him. He's a heroin user who sleeps with women other than her. She doesn't know if he has AIDS, but doesn't question him because she is completely enamored with their relationship.

Women's Feelings about Condoms

Let's take a look at condoms and AIDS transmission. Condoms apparently lower the risk of contracting AIDS, at least in the laboratory, if used with a spermicide, Nonoxynol-9. They must also be used correctly: to be put on before any exchange of body fluid occurs; to be put on the penis with a space left at the tip; to remove the penis after ejaculation before removing the condom. Even employing all of these safety measures, condoms are not one hundred percent effective.

If one engages in sex with a person who has AIDS, I believe the risk is too great to take, even using a condom. Condoms have a 10 percent failure rate. Contraception studies were conducted on the use of condoms for a one-year period that was the basis for the 10 percent failure rate (*Journal of the American Medical Association,* February 1987). This means that one out of ten women, who regularly use condoms as a method of birth control, becomes pregnant in a one-year time frame, even if the condom remains intact during intercourse and doesn't break.

A woman could get AIDS if some infected fluid from a man's damp pubic hair touches her genitals. Most sexual experiences, even using a condom, involve some exchange of body fluids between the moist genital areas and body openings. The moist skin and secretions of the AIDS-infected person contain large concentrations of the virus. The AIDS virus can enter a woman's body if it comes into contact with mucous membranes that are found in the mouth, nose, nipples, rectum, and genital organs. It is even very likely that these secretions are exchanged when a couple cuddles together, after making love.

Condom or no condom, sexual intercourse is an extremely dangerous practice if one of the partners is infected with the AIDS virus. My hope is that there will be less emphasis placed on condoms, and more emphasis placed on not having sex until one is certain one's sexual partner is not infected. The use of condoms as an AIDS protective measure is exaggerated and can lead to a false sense of security.

Following, are several women's opinions on condoms in regard to AIDS:

Harriet Barrett: "Hallelujah! Great! It's out of the closet—out of the drawers. We don't know more on how to decrease the risks, so I'm glad condoms are a tool to use. I watched a television program and macho men still don't wear them. They say, 'It doesn't feel good.' I'm glad condoms are out there for those to use, who never did. It's one more person covered. On a scale of one to ten, I would rate it a four. It's not the perfect solution, but we're getting there."

Patricia: "Condoms serve a dual purpose. Not only as a source of AIDS prevention, but as a form of birth control, too. It also stops the spread of other venereal disease. You may not prevent spreading AIDS, but you stop a pregnancy, and the birth of a child with AIDS."

Michelle T.: "Condoms are supposed to have a ten percent failure rate, but if used properly, they're better than nothing. People lose a lot of sexuality when there's no exchange of body fluid. This is the sad part. Abstinence would be best, but realistically, I don't see teenagers being abstinent. I hope they, at least, have less sexual partners."

Denise: "People should not be told that by using condoms, everything will be okay. Condoms lower the risk, at least in the laboratory, and that is a start. But I think that it's too dangerous to tell people, especially adolescents, that by using condoms, you have nothing to worry about. AIDS is a fatal disease and I believe that condoms are not the answer. I became pregnant a few years ago when using a condom to prevent pregnancy! They are not 100 percent effective against pregnancy, so I know they are also not 100 percent effective in preventing the transmission of AIDS.

"I think that people must be told to look at relationships and the issues of being sure of your partner. This is a long-term process that is particularly hard for kids who are just embarking on sexual journeys and don't want to hear about AIDS and dying. Kids have to learn that condoms aren't the answer. The answer lies in mutual trust and believing in the other person in a relationship. You can't go out and have sex freely with anyone you desire without thinking about AIDS.

"I think many people look at condoms as the panacea against AIDS. This is a scary thought. It's also a tragic situation because the people who are careful really can't have sex unless they take the long road to finding out if it's safe. It's certainly affected me. Although I don't have a sexual relationship, I would like to. I'm afraid."

The threat of heterosexual AIDS transmission exists. AIDS does not discriminate. People who have not known someone who has died as a result of AIDS are not directly affected by the disease, and as a result, the disease is not a reality. Despite the daily media bombardment of AIDS facts and figures, the reality is that most middle-class heterosexuals do not feel at any great risk for getting AIDS. If I had not been exposed to AIDS through the death of a friend, I too, would most likely have this attitude. But this is not the right attitude to have. Everyone is at risk, everyone is affected by AIDS, and one's behavior should reflect that this be a time of caution for all. Some counselors have not been directly affected by AIDS but should be aware that this is a false sense of security that many women hold.

The next chapter is for counselors and everyone who must deal with feelings and fears about AIDS.

5

For Counselors and Everyone: Dealing with Our Feelings and Fears

Before one can help others one must learn how to confront one's own fears particularly in regard to AIDS. No matter how rational and levelheaded some claim to be, especially in their professional lives as counselors, unexpected overreactions are not uncommon when faced with this illness that has such horrible consequences if contracted. People must face issues that may normally make them uncomfortable such as homosexuality, drug abuse, sexually transmitted disease, sexuality, and death. Not only must they face these issues but they must learn to become comfortable enough to talk about them as well.

Many people experience instances of panic in situations where AIDS is involved. Although I know that AIDS is not easy to get (there have been no documented cases to date of AIDS transmitted through casual contact), there are still moments of obsession in regard to the time spent with Sebastian three years ago in the hospital, and the likelihood of my having AIDS. I hugged, rubbed, and massaged Sebastian to bring down fevers. I wiped mucus away from his mouth. I kissed him and held his hand. We were as physically intimate as two people can be without having sexual contact. Did I have a cut on my hand? A torn cuticle? Did I wipe my eyes before washing my hands? etc., etc. It becomes easy to be obsessed with catching a disease that is fatal. No matter how educated one may be on the subject of AIDS, these reactions can still occur. When I overreact, I try to acknowledge my fears and then find someone to talk to. It helps to get some objective feedback. If I were left to my own subjective irrationality, panic would most likely be the result!

Think about the nurse who works with AIDS patients, starting IVs, changing bedclothes, washing patients, emptying catheter bags and bedpans many times in the course of a day. Imagine how easy it might be for this nurse to fear getting AIDS. Realistically, nurses have to face AIDS on a daily basis, coming into contact with body fluids and taking risks that most of us would not be exposed to.

One of the nurses interviewed stated that she is tested for AIDS antibodies every few months just as a precaution. Her husband insists she change her clothes in the garage and shower before she comes into contact with the family! This woman must deal with her own fears and her husband's also. She says she is able to make allowances for the overreactions of her husband and willingly complies with his request in order to keep sanity in her relationship. Her outlet is through a women's discussion group of nurses who face similar difficulties. Again, feedback from others helps put our fears in perspective.

A psychologist tells of the fear she experienced in regard to a client who had AIDS. When the therapy session ends the psychologist gets the bleach and wipes every surface that came in contact with her client; doorknobs, couch, chair, etc. Although this professional is well-briefed and knowledgeable about AIDS, she cannot resist disinfecting her office. She is completely aware that she is overreacting and is embarrassed to say so. But, she has taken the first step in coping with her irrational behavior by talking about it with another person. Awareness and the ability to admit one's fears are tantamount to overcoming them. This is not always easy to do. When one is capable of sharing feelings, a perspective can be reached. When one remains alone, unable to talk about one's fear, it can fester and become more out of proportion.

During the time spent with Sebastian as he was dying, a woman friend who had come to the hospital asked if she could talk to me before returning home. She was embarrassed to ask me if I thought she could give AIDS to her husband and children. Should she shower and change clothes before coming in contact with her family? Sebastian's death occurred three years ago and at that time we knew little about AIDS. I reassured her that she would not infect her family, although I wasn't altogether certain myself. If she had not been able to talk to someone about her very frightening concerns, she may have returned home with the fear that she would infect her entire family. It took courage to express these feelings.

Some people are unwilling to share their feelings, not out of fear of embarrassment but because they think they're right. This can lead to prejudice. Prejudice can be as deadly as AIDS itself. Take, for example, the Florida family who was burned out of their home and had to move to another town. The family had three hemophiliac children who got AIDS through contaminated blood products. Apparently, some of their "neighbors" set the fire. One or all of the family members may have been injured or killed in the fire that was caused by prejudiced people.

Panic and prejudice were feelings common to a group of teachers I spoke to. These professionals had learned that a child with AIDS might be admitted into their school. One teacher feared touching the child or an object that the child might handle. The nurse was afraid to administer to the child's needs should a cut, scrape, or bloody nose occur. The music teacher was concerned about how to decontaminate a musical instrument played by the child. The most adamant of the group was a teacher who threatened resignation if the child was admitted into the school. Most of these reactions were out of proportion to the context of AIDS and how it is transmitted but, nevertheless, were real concerns expressed by these teachers. At least they were able to verbalize their fears and to get feedback from others. The sharing of concerns helped to bring these reactions into perspective for the majority of the teachers with the exception of the one who would resign if the child were admitted. He would not allow himself to be reached.

During a recent AIDS presentation to a group of social workers, I was surprised by a majority of the attendants' reactions to my story about Sebastian. I told the group that Sebastian had stayed with me a few weeks prior to his death, but did not tell me he had AIDS. The group participants responded with anger toward Sebastian. They said it was his duty and responsibility to let me know he had AIDS. They thought he had jeopardized myself and my family by staying in my house. I had a difficult time responding to this angry reaction from a group of educated professionals. They repeatedly asked why I was not angry at Sebastian for his inconsiderate and even life-threatening behavior to me. This was one instance where I felt uncomfortable because of being put on the defensive and under unexpected attack. I reassured the group that I was not angry and had no cause to be since AIDS is not transmitted in a casual manner. I was only angry that a person as beautiful as he had died such a horrible death. I don't know if I convinced these people of my true feelings but hope that they at least thought about my response.

Prejudice has taken the form of neighborhood opposition to a counseling center for AIDS people in Queens. When the center first opened (in February 1987) vandals threw rocks through its windows and telephone callers threatened to firebomb the building. The neighborhood was frightened because a large portion of people with AIDS are drug users and homosexuals, and the high school is one and a half blocks from the center.

An area church leader defended the center and said that this is a pure and simple form of prejudice against the victims of AIDS who are generally either homosexuals or drug users. The New York City Human Rights Commission has become involved (*New York Times*, Sunday, March 13, 1988).

Here is an example of fear getting in the way of understanding. A lack of compassion results in discrimination against a group of people who have so much need of understanding. I don't have any easy answers for this situation. It's unfortunate that some people cannot talk about their fears before negatively acting upon them.

Mary, a caseworker for an agency that places children in foster homes, tells of lack of communication from the bureaucratic level, which results in personal misunderstanding and frustration.

Mary: "My job at the agency often involves transporting a child to a foster family." In particular was the case of T., an eight-month-old baby, who had been placed with a foster family. T. was constantly sick, developmentally delayed, and he cried all the time. He had chronic thrush infections, bronchial infections, and appeared to fail to thrive. T. was much smaller than an average eight-month-old. The family who had him also cared for other children and just felt they couldn't handle T., with his many medical problems.

"Our agency found another foster placement for T. I transported him to his new home. I knew his mother was a drug user and I was convinced that he had AIDS from the symptoms of his illnesses. What bothered me most, aside from the tragedy of his illness, was my lack of information about him. After all, I was to feed him, change his diapers, and handle him for several hours en route. I should have been told by the agency that the child had AIDS. I had to take my own initiative, assume he had AIDS, and handle him so that I felt comfortable.

"As we drove to his new foster home, T., in his car seat, coughed and sneezed and several times I had to wipe his nose and face. I know that I got mucus on my hands. I also changed his diaper and since we were in the car, I couldn't wash my hands afterward. During the entire trip I was acutely aware of the possibility of contracting AIDS because of poor hygiene, even though I know the disease is not supposed to be spread that way.

"I had taken a bag of lunch for the trip. Even after washing my hands I was afraid to eat my lunch. I had this irrational fear that I hadn't disinfected myself enough to prevent getting the disease.

"It's funny—this is the first I've talked about my reactions. I guess I was embarrassed before but my fears passed. It probably would have been easier if I had someone to talk to when the incident occurred but I came through it."

An extreme example of unreasonable fear and discrimination of AIDS hysteria was reported by the *New York Times*, Monday, March 14, 1988. Texas realtors were advised to tell a prospective buyer if a house had been inhabited by someone with AIDS. The Texas Association of Realtors has told members that prior occupancy by a person with AIDS may be viewed by some buyers as a house defect similar to the presence of radon gas, a bad roof, or a leaky basement. Real-estate agents were advised to disclose such information to a prospective buyer to avoid a lawsuit.

It is believed that the Texas association is the first group of realtors to make a recommendation on AIDS. California is the only state with legislation on AIDS. The law prohibits real-estate agents from inquiring about AIDS or disclosing AIDS information to prospective buyers.

The Texas realtors now bring AIDS confidentiality issues to the forefront opening the pathway to discrimination. No other disease is singled out in regard to house sales.

John Paul Barnich, legal counsel and acting chairman for the Houston AIDS Foundation, says, "It's just the most recent and blatant example of AIDS hysteria. If realtors are asked to furnish information on AIDS patients, they can be required to furnish medical records on every person that has ever lived there."

The Texas group officials say that they are not implicating a health risk from inhabiting the home of a prior AIDS person, but if a potential buyer has a strong fear of AIDS and would not buy a house if a person with AIDS lived there, the realtor could face legal liability for the misrepresentation of information.

My opinion on the stance taken by the Texas group is that it feeds prejudice, discrimination, and is a violation of human rights. It also promotes hysteria that cannot be a benefit to anyone. If there were even a trace of realistic health risk in living in a house occupied by someone who has AIDS, I would have more understanding for the plight of the realtors.

Sue W., a social worker and mother, had to face her fears about AIDS after learning that a colleague tested HIV positive.

Sue W: "When K. came to work and told us she tested positive for the AIDS virus, I went into shock. I've known and worked with this woman for seven years. How could she have AIDS? She doesn't look sick. She's had a cough for a while but she's a smoker. My doctor later told me that a dry, nonproductive cough is one of the symptoms of AIDS.

"At the office now, there is all of this tremendous grief, sorrow, and pain. It's very hard to cope with. I can't talk to K. without breaking down and after I speak to her, then there's this other thing—like should I share a coffee cup.

Horrible things, and I know it's been said you can't get AIDS this way but I can't help myself. One day K. was sitting at her desk, coughing, sneezing, and wiping her nose. I noticed and freaked out. I looked at her and said, 'K., that bothers me.' 'You can't get it like this,' she said. 'I know, but you should be aware, that's all.' I cried for an hour after I said this to her, thinking what a horrible person I was. I thought that anybody with a cold shouldn't be sneezing and coughing all over everything so why couldn't she be extra careful?

"I think there's a tendency for people who have AIDS to almost say, 'Will you still love me?' It's like testing the limits. What I found out in this situation is that I have limits. I put myself before others. I have a family.

"My friend said, 'Well, I love K. and I feel that I must show my love by not being afraid of anything.' I said, 'You're off-the-wall!' I feel that I must show my love to myself and to my family and that there are certain ways in which I need to feel safe. I would never say K. shouldn't come to work, that's not necessary, but I also feel that she should be extra careful around others."

Sue had to define boundaries in which to feel safe when faced with a threatening situation. Although she feels devastated by knowing her friend has AIDS, she also has the courage to speak out and say what makes her uncomfortable. Communicating her fears to her friend, no matter how unreasonable they may seem, opened the line of interaction between the two, thus resulting in understanding.

For those who have difficulty voicing their fears because they feel stupid or don't want to appear vulnerable, it's a good idea to practice on a friend. Try talking to a friend or family member when something bothers you, no matter how insignificant it may appear. Practice will make you more able to confront the big issues that involve AIDS.

Finally, a way to deal with feelings and alleviate prejudice on a large scale is public exposure to AIDS issues through the media and through AIDS benefits. In particular, when well-known, credible people become involved with benefits for AIDS, everyone stands up and listens. Rock Hudson, who first openly acknowledged his gender preference and the fact that he had AIDS, made AIDS real to the general public. Hudson's death put AIDS into perspective for those who thought only drug addicts and homosexuals could get the disease.

Liz Taylor's involvement with AIDS benefits has also helped the fight against the illness. Broadway theater groups continue to raise money for AIDS research. The music industry stages concerts to obtain AIDS funding. Writers groups are involved with AIDS benefits. Bookstores are donating a percentage of sales of selected books to AIDS research. This widespread interest from well-known people in raising money for AIDS continues to provide a positive example to humanity that will hopefully alleviate many of the unrealistic fears and prejudices surrounding the disease.

Counselors and therapists have an important role in desensitizing the panic that accompanies AIDS. By providing a forum within counseling sessions where people's concerns can be addressed, realistic caution can be separated from irrational and undue panic.

Talking to women about AIDS is presented in the following chapter with particular emphasis on how to be an effective and empathetic helper.

6

Counseling Issues:
Talking to Women about AIDS

Many people, whether they are social workers, psychologists, teachers, doctors, nurses, etc., will be called upon to guide and to provide leadership to women who have AIDS or to the family and friends of people with AIDS. The best treatment builds on the person's past coping abilities, capitalizes on strengths, maintains hope, and shows continued care and concern for the person needing help.

Before one can be helpful one must become familiar and comfortable with the many issues that people who have AIDS will most likely experience. Untimely death, prejudice, stigma, isolation, loneliness, loss of employment, physical and emotional pain, and fear are the prevalent aspects that someone with AIDS must face. People who are helpers need to be sensitive to all of these issues, and to be empathic and positive besides. This is a tall order for both the helpers and the people who need help, and I don't suggest it's easy to do.

For the helpers, the first step can be to learn about AIDS: what it is, how it's transmitted and prevented, basic truths and untruths, so that they have the general knowledge to talk to others about the disease (see chapter 3—"What Is AIDS?").

They also need to understand the scope of the psychological aspects surrounding the disease, both for the afflicted and their family and friends. The helpers need to know specific concerns that women have about the disease. Because so many people are frightened of contracting the disease, they fear being around those who have it. This in itself is an isolating/stigmatizing behavior that promotes emotional pain in people who have AIDS. For further discussion see chapter 3 for psychological issues.

Professional counselors, i.e., psychologists, psychiatrists, social workers, go to school to learn psychotherapeutic techniques to help people. I will present some basic concepts of how to talk to women based on Gerard Egan's humanistic counseling approach from his book, *The Skilled Helper*, which I find to be a comfortable and practical method when helping others.

First, it is beneficial to develop rapport with the person you are trying to help. This can be established through attentive behaviors that show you are a good listener. Eye contact and an attitude of interest toward the person shows you are there for them. Looking at your watch or out the window will not promote a good relationship. If you are not comfortable with what is being said, it will be evident to the other person. Again, I stress the importance of awareness of the core issues that a person with AIDS will experience, so that you will not reveal shock or surprise.

Your ability to be there and to share common experiences is tantamount to the establishment of the relationship. For example, I have often shared the death of my friend Sebastian from an AIDS-related illness with those whom I try to help. I believe this puts me on a similar level, lending credibility to the relationship. When you show that you too have been devastated because of AIDS, a common bond is formed. Don't be afraid to let your feelings show. You are vulnerable also, and it's good to show that you're both in this together.

The most devastating problems involving AIDS can be

handled more effectively with the assistance of a good helper. The goal of helping is to assist others in managing life's problems, if only just a little bit better. Remember, as a helper, one is not expected to make everything all right. It's not possible, and you will be setting yourself up for failure before you begin. If your assistance can alleviate only a small amount of pain, you will be successful.

The following case of Jean will be presented so that counselors can have guidelines when helping a woman with AIDS.

Jean was horrified when a doctor told her that she tested positive for the AIDS virus. She had visited her doctor two weeks earlier because she was tired all the time and had consented to an AIDS test as a matter of routine, never really thinking that she'd been exposed to the virus. She thought she was run-down from working too hard. How could this be? How did she get it? She was only thirty-two years old, too young to die. What about her five-year-old daughter? Will she test HIV positive too? Who will care for her if Jean should develop AIDS and die? She felt disbelief, anger, and despair. After many angry confrontations with family and doctors, she agreed to see a counselor. The fact that Jean tests positive for the AIDS virus does not necessarily mean that she will develop full-blown AIDS. On the other hand, there is no guarantee that she won't develop the disease sometime in the future. Jean is in a terrifying and compromising position. At this point, there is a tremendous amount of pressure on her to be the major support system for her daughter. With help, Jean will learn to cope with the possibility that she might contract AIDS, and will actually find friends who will take her daughter, in case of her death.

In this case, Jean might get AIDS and die. The helper will not be able to prevent it or to make everything all right.

Let's assume that you, the reader, are the helper who will assist Jean during the painful process of coming to terms with the possibility of death, and the consequences of leaving her daughter behind.

In the first stage of the helping process, Jean needs to define her fears and problems. She needs to clarify all the possibilities that may happen to her and her daughter. To be a good helper, you can use various skills in order to develop your relationship with Jean so that she trusts you. Good rapport is essential and can be achieved by taking the time to listen attentively when Jean describes her problems. Look for nonverbal messages such as body posture, lack of eye contact, and other nervous gestures that may reveal how Jean is feeling as you respond to her conversation. Listen carefully; if you do not understand what is being said say so. As conversation progresses, show that you understand what is being said in order to clarify the issues. AIDS victims may feel that they did something to cause the disease, or they may attribute it to bad luck or "God." You can help Jean accept the fact that she did not bring on the disease because she is a bad person.

As Jean's helper, you must maintain confidences and respect her values even if they are not your own. A judgmental helper will not be an effective helper. For example: Jean confides that in her past, she used IV drugs. You may not approve of IV drug use but it will be detrimental to reveal your stance on this issue. In general, there are many social taboos such as homosexuality, sexually transmitted disease, and drug abuse, which may have to be broached when involved with talk about AIDS. If the helper cannot learn to be comfortable talking about these issues, he or she will not be successful. The first stage of the helping process is complete when a solid foundation of trust, empathy, and respect has been established between the helper and Jean.

The second stage of interaction is to find ways in which to help Jean realistically manage her problems. The helper can assist Jean in setting goals. Before this can happen, Jean needs to explore all aspects of her problem, putting it into perspective and integrating the information so as to form reasonable goals. The helper should become familiar with five challenging skills, which may be helpful in assisting Jean to set realistic goals. These beneficial skills, designated by Gerard Egan in his book *The Skilled Helper*, are discussed as follows:

The first skill is *information sharing*. Jean's main concern is the welfare of her daughter. At this point, she is terrified that she will infect her daughter with the AIDS virus. Jean doesn't have all the facts on how AIDS is transmitted, and she is overreacting. An important role for the helper is to share information on how AIDS is contracted and transmitted, to put Jean's fears into perspective. She should be told that it is okay to have physical contact with her daughter. She can also prepare food for her daughter without the fear of infection. Most important, the daughter can be tested for the presence of AIDS antibodies.

The second challenging skill is *advanced accurate empathy*, which is expressing to Jean what she has implied in her conversation. This is not to be confused with primary empathy, which is understanding Jean's point of view and simply reflecting it back to her. Consider the following helper's responses to Jean's statement in order to understand the difference between the two empathy skills.

JEAN: I generally call my mother every week but I've put if off since learning that I tested positive for the AIDS virus. I'm afraid she'll call me before too long.

HELPER A: It seems that you're afraid that your mother will call because you usually call her every week and she hasn't heard from you.

HELPER B: Unless I'm mistaken, it sounds like you're not prepared to tell your mother about your illness at this time.

Helper A is using primary empathy to simply reflect back to Jean the message that she put forth. Helper B based her response on what Jean implied in her statement (advanced empathy). Jean did not directly say that she is not ready to confront her mother with her illness, but the implication is there. As a helper, it is okay to take a chance and read between the lines. Sensitivity and intuition are important aspects of the helping process. But beware, you can carry your response too far by assuming more than what is implied. Your inaccuracy and false assumptions can be detrimental to the helping situation. Take, for example, helper C's response to Jean's previous statement:

HELPER C: It sounds like you're afraid to tell your mother about your illness because she will think less of you after learning that you got AIDS as a result of drug abuse.

Helper C is inserting her own judgment into Jean's statement, incorrectly assuming what was implied. This insensitive response may very well destroy the trust and rapport that has been established to this point in the relationship. As a helper, do not imply unless you are relatively sure that you are correct. Use your intuition and sensitivity but do not be judgmental.

The third challenging skill is *confrontation*. You can use confrontation to bring inconsistencies, distortions, and discrepancies to the surface during Jean's interactions with you and her family/friends and colleagues. Confrontation is used to examine types of behavior that appear to be self-defeating, and to change those behaviors.

For example, during Jean's conversations with her helper she always says she is fine, but is obviously confused and feeling a lot of distress. A sensitive helper might confront Jean's discrepant behavior in this way:

HELPER: Jean, you always say you're fine, but when I see you, you seem nervous and not very happy. Is there more to how you are feeling? I wonder what might be keeping you from talking about it?

JEAN: I'm not feeling well at all but I'm afraid I'll break down and loose control if I get into it.

In this example of confrontation, the helper gently reminded Jean that her behavior was incompatible with her words. As a result, she finally admitted why she was afraid to talk about it.

A fourth challenging skill is *helper self-sharing*. To be an effective helper, you must be willing to share your own experiences if you feel they may be of help. Be careful not to place too much burden on the other person.

For example, Jean is experiencing prejudice from a family member who said, "What did you expect from your days of drug abuse? I feel sorry for you but you should have known better than to get involved with drugs in the first place." This insensitive statement has left Jean devastated. If I were Jean's helper, I might share a similar experience.

When my friend died of an AIDS-related illness, I stopped to see a member of my family on my way home from the hospital. I was very much in need of caring, support, and a hug. Instead, I received, "What did you expect? You knew that he was a homosexual." Needless to say, this uncaring and insensitive remark was completely unexpected, and I was devastated.

Sharing this similar experience with Jean provided a

common bond between us. It was helpful to let her know that she isn't the only one who has experienced prejudice and insensitivity.

The final challenging skill is *immediacy* or the willingness to explore what is happening in the interaction between the helper and the person being helped. Use the relationship as a starting point in order to help Jean to better understand herself and how she relates to others. Immediacy is a difficult skill to master because many of us have never learned how to have direct, mutual talk. This skill relates to self-involvement and mutuality. If you are having difficulty with intimacy in your own life, you can expect to have trouble with this skill.

Following is an example of how people fail to be immediate with one another during interaction:

A wife is hurt by something her husband says. Rather than say so, she avoids talking about it. She becomes quieter and more uncommunicative over the next few days. Little things her husband does become irritating, and finally a large argument occurs. They make up, but both feel somewhat childish and guilty about the confrontation.

Let's look at how the use of immediacy can be helpful in regard to a trust issue between Jean and her helper. Jean appears ill at ease and is not being communicative with her helper.

HELPER: Jean, you seem uncomfortable and hesitant. I'm not sure if it has to do with me or not. Maybe it's still difficult for you to trust me.

JEAN: I do feel uncomfortable but mostly I trust you. It's just that I want to talk about my days of drug use, and I've had nothing but judgmental reactions from anyone I've ever talked to about it. I don't want you to judge me too.

In this situation, the helper sensed that Jean was uncomfortable and successfully used immediacy to clarify the problem.

In summary: the second stage of helping is complete when the helper has successfully assisted Jean in the realistic definitions of her problems in regard to AIDS. You are now ready to set the goals for the final stage of the helping process.

Facilitating Goals

Effective helping is not only talking and planning. Jean must act upon and actually implement the goals that she wants to attain. You, as Jean's helper, can assist her in developing a list of programs that will provide comfortable choices to fit her needs.

Jean wants to take part in an experimental drug program for people who have AIDS. You can help her choose an appropriate program that involves women by contacting the Centers for Disease Control or the National Institute of Health (see the appendix for listings). At this time, most of the AIDS clinical trials have male patients, but with the increasing number of women who have AIDS, this is changing.

Jean has decided to participate in a support group for women who have AIDS. Fears and frustrations can be alleviated by sharing experiences with others who have similar problems. Call local AIDS hot lines to find counselors who specify in AIDS-related therapy (see the appendix for resources).

Jean's ultimate concern is the welfare of her daughter. The child has been tested for AIDS antibodies and the results are negative. If Jean develops AIDS and dies, she needs to find a home for her daughter. She may need help in choosing a legal guardian and implementing legal procedures. The Gay Men's Health Crisis is an excellent resource for assistance in legal matters that involve AIDS. See the appendix for phone listings.

Jean's story is a simplified but true version of what a woman and mother must face when confronted with the reality of AIDS. The reader as helper has been provided with some basic counseling skills on how to talk to a woman who needs help in dealing with the tragic situation of AIDS.

Helping the Helper

Helpers are as involved with the emotions and feelings that surround AIDS as are the women they are trying to help. Their attitudes and reactions involved with the helping relationship can be rooted in past relationships. This is called countertransference, a psychoanalytic term used to describe some of the frustration and impasse that occur in counseling. The helper can attempt to utilize rather than deny these feelings that can be a powerful tool in the helping relationship.

As the helper, remember to take care of yourself. You too are human, are vulnerable, and have feelings. Acknowledge your emotions; don't deny them. You may feel anger because AIDS is a fatal disese that you cannot cure. Don't keep these feelings hidden. You will not be able to effectively help others if you hide or become bogged down in anger or sorrow. AIDS is here and all must cope with it the best they can through sharing, doing, and expressing their feelings for themselves and others.

Counselors/helpers: For further discussion on how AIDS affects women, see the following chapter.

7

How AIDS Affects Women

The presence of AIDS is having an effect on many women's lives and life-styles, particularly single women and those involved with others who have AIDS. Knowing these effects is helpful to counselors. In researching this book, women were interviewed in regard to how AIDS has affected their lives. The responses varied, and were sad, touching, and shocking.

Jan M., New York State resident and elementary-school teacher, has been profoundly affected by the presence of AIDS in her everyday life.

"Until a few months ago, I could say that AIDS hadn't really affected me in a personal way. I had empathy for people who had the disease but didn't know anyone who was sick. I attended AIDS workshops in the school and thought I was prepared should one of the students become infected. I was not prepared when informed by the school social worker that one of my third-grade students had a mother who was very sick with AIDS. I watched this little boy become withdrawn, defensive, and sad. My heart ached for him and the pressures he was experiencing at home. I felt so helpless and wished I could do more to ease his pain. He did not mention that his mother had AIDS and didn't know that I knew the true nature of his mother's illness.

"Last week his mother died and he didn't return to

school. I was told that he went to live with relatives in New York City. I'm left feeling helpless and can only hope that his relatives love him and will be good to him. Now I wait for the next time because I'm sure there will be many more sad experiences like this one."

Ex-nurse and mother, Michelle T., has been affected by AIDS in several ways.

"AIDS has definitely influenced the way I view relationships. I have single friends and it's difficult to be single at this point. It's hard to even discuss AIDS with my friends because it's such a loaded topic. I almost feel guilty that I'm married and not in a position to start a new relationship! But I would like to think that as an adult, I would be forthright and insist on condoms, and sleep around less than I did. AIDS has made a huge impact socially. It seems to be on everyone's mind.

"AIDS has also made a more dramatic impact on my future career choices. Although I have not practiced nursing for three years, since my daughter was born, I thought I might go back to it in a few years when she's a little older. I used to work in the emergency room where the main concern was to save people's lives. There wasn't time for gloves and masks; you didn't use them. The first priority was to get an IV in. You went through blood, vomitus. Everything you could possibly be touching. Your main concern was to save a person's life, not protect yourself from a disease. Unfortunately, if I went back to nursing, I would have to reconsider riding an ambulance, and that's sad. It seems that there's just too much possibility of direct contact and possible infection with HIV for me to make that choice again. If I didn't have children, maybe."

Barbara, nurse and single mother, thinks about AIDS everyday.

"I think about AIDS a lot and I'm more cautious about

a lot of things. Right now, I'm not in a relationship but if I was, AIDS would be something for me to worry about . . . like who else have they been with?

"At work, everybody's more cautious; they wear gloves. I don't wear them all the time. Because of my work I come in contact with many different people's blood . . . starting IVs . . . you worry because if you get stuck with a needle, it won't matter how many pairs of gloves you have on; it's going to go through. I am worried about needle sticks but we had to worry about that before because of hepatitis. But AIDS is more of a concern than any other illness because you can die!

"The first time we had somebody in the hospital **with** AIDS, about four years ago, nobody wanted to go near them. I have taken care of several people with AIDS since then and I still get nervous because people sick with AIDS need intravenous medication and there's always that possibility of a needle stick. All it takes is the slip of your hand.

"Recently, there have been three women who come to the hospital that test positive for HIV. There's one who's a prostitute and IV drug user. I hope she's still not working! But she's been in and out of the hospital several times with pneumonia. I don't know what kind of follow-up is being done with her but it's possible she's spreading it [AIDS] around. All the others with AIDS have since died."

May, nurse and mother, has worked in the prison system with inmates who had AIDS.

"AIDS has affected me both in my job as a nurse, and in my daily living with my family. In the prison, I often had to work with men who were hooked up to IV therapy with a line going directly into their bloodstream. When I had to unhook those lines, I sometimes got blood on me and thought, 'Oh my God, now what?' It was a scary situation.

"I don't want to put the prisons down, but there was no

policy for the nurses to follow. Some of the men would drool or have some drainage from their mouth, and they would get nasty and spit at the nurses. This was a new way to get back at prison personnel.

"They say AIDS can't be transferred through saliva, tears, or urine, but who really knows? Supposedly you can only get it from direct contact with an open wound but I didn't know that when I worked with these men. One time I got stuck in the finger with a needle taken from someone who had AIDS. I washed it out immediately, but I'm afraid to get tested because if I have it, what can I do? It's better not to know. Should I isolate myself from my family or kill myself? If I do have it, it's too late anyway.

"One of the nurses I know gave mouth-to-mouth to a man who subsequently died of AIDS, but she didn't know he had AIDS when she gave it to him. She wasn't even notified when he died. She didn't get tested either because she had just had a baby and was too frightened to find out.

"I get scared of all the contact I've had with AIDS patients and then feel guilty because what if I infected my family? I try not to think about it. I block it out or else I would go crazy.

"It was horrible to watch those men with AIDS in the prison. I think a lot of us have hardened feelings for criminals, but what if you look at that person as your mother or father? Maybe they got it from a transfusion and not from the adverse ways that people always associate with AIDS. It doesn't mean that you're immoral or an addict if you get AIDS. If a little boy gets AIDS, people think right away that his mother is an addict. I think the public sees AIDS from a 'dirty' perspective and doesn't believe that innocent people can get it, that you're not a bad person if you get it.

"Something I worry about from the prison is the kitchen

where inmates cook food for the guards. Some of the inmates that worked in the kitchen had AIDS but were not sick yet. What if one of the men cut his finger and dripped it on the food? I know it's said that the virus would die in this situation, but who really knows? Has anybody eaten food contaminated with AIDS and then been tested to see if they got it? How can they test in a situation like this?

"My father-in-law had open-heart surgery nine years ago. He lost a lot of blood and was given several pints to make up for the blood he lost. I worry about him today and think about the chance of that blood being contaminated with the AIDS virus.

"I'm on the first-aid rescue squad and what happens if someone has a heart attack? Would I put my mouth on his? What if he vomits? I would hesitate in this situation to help, but I carry my AMBU bag in case this happens. If I didn't have that bag, I wouldn't do cardiac massage.

"One thing I worry about because I have children, is a child who gets AIDS. Do you tell them or lie to them about dying? Do you help them die with dignity or do you let them go on in a fantasy world, not knowing if they're going to get better or not? I don't know if I could accept that."

Patricia, single, social worker: "AIDS has definitely affected my life-style. Right now I'm not in a relationship with anyone. In fact, the disease is so scary to me that I don't know what I will do if I meet someone I want to have a relationship with. Just today I heard on the news that even if you only have ARC, it will definitely develop into full-blown AIDS; it's just a matter of time. Anyone who is infected with the HIV virus is going to die according to the CDC. Now I know for sure I don't want to be tested for the virus. Who in their right mind wants to know they are going to die? Especially when it's just a matter of time.

"The disease hasn't affected my work to date but I'm certain it will in the near future. I work with people who are IV drug users; many of them live in the Bronx. I have been told that the statistics show that ninety-five percent of the IV drug users in the Bronx that are female are infected with the disease. If this is the truth, then most of the women I work with are going to die. If you really want to dwell on it, you can drive yourself nuts!"

I was particularly touched by Cora's story of her loss of a younger brother to an AIDS-related illness, and how this event profoundly changed her life.

Cora, mother and homemaker: "I lost a dearly loved brother to AIDS. When he died, I lost my closest friend. His death left a great gap in my life and a rage to know that there was so little research done when it was known years ago that AIDS was around. Even as the statistics came rolling in, the government gave minimum funds and appointed a committee to study AIDS, half of which were not qualified to do so; a farce and a token gesture.

"The part of my brother's life that left him vulnerable to AIDS never caused me to judge him. I loved him as he was. It is absolutely amazing to hear comments from people on how the disease is the plague for the godless, etc. All I can say is though I may find people in our church with such thoughts, they are a minority so small. What I do find are people who care to want to do something, and feel a human bond with those who have it. On the other hand, all those feelings of care get mixed in with a fear of AIDS. It has been around longer than we knew, and society has changed so in regard to openness and physical relationships. Now the unspoken fear is, 'Do I have the virus from my days of roaming around?' I hear this from college students and single adults of all ages. Relationships are now changing for many to back to where we were in the fifties.

"The toll that AIDS will take in human lives will be, I fear, higher than statistically given. But the toll in the intellectual and creative genius in the fields of art, music, dance, etc. will leave us empty for voices we always took for granted.

"My feelings when my brother was in the hospital were, 'Not my brother, please.' One thing I did find interesting and remember teasing him about was that he didn't want me to come to the hospital. He said he'd be home soon. Of course, I went to see him in the hospital and spoke with him that very first evening. I told him that I knew he had AIDS, and that we'll beat it together. I told him he was loved by many and asked if I could call his friends to tell them. He was hesitant with what I felt was a fear of being judged, but then he wrote the names of people to call. The last thing he wrote, (he couldn't talk because of the respirator), which I will always treasure was, 'together—you love me no matter.' I then contacted his friends and at times sat with a glass of wine as I spoke to as many as I could, feeling numb. Somehow I did it and it was with my faith in God and the love of my brother that I put aside my own hurt. I remember telling my children, 'I'll crack later. Now I have to hang in and keep it all together.'

"The hardest for me was having to speak to my youngest child. He was seven then. It was Monday night and I stayed home alone with him so that I could tell him that his uncle was dying. He knew but was afraid to say it. I cracked that evening. We cried together and I listened to his anger: how he only had him for such a short time, how it wasn't fair. When we stopped crying, we spoke of some of the joyous days we shared with him, saying that we would always hold onto them. Before I rocked him to sleep my son said, 'God must have needed someone who knew how to love people and make them laugh, because when He looks at the news, He must cry.' That statement has brought me great consolation. At times, I can envision a scenario of the life beyond with my brother making everyone laugh. It does bring a smile to me.

"My brother's life was a gift of love and caring, the

thoughtful things he would do, the surprises he would plan, and that absolute twinkle in his eye.

"What I did learn is that you tell someone they are loved and special in your life. My brother knew he was. I did not have to stand beside a hospital bed and say it to him, figuring all along that he knew he was treasured. The words didn't have to be said. I always talk about him if the feeling arises or I negate the fact that he existed. Last, but most important, is that there is a light at the end, and there is really no end but just a new beginning. I have no fear of dying, just how it will happen gets to me."

Talking to Cora was a touching experience. She went through the painful ordeal of losing a beloved brother, but came through with less fear and a lot of lovely memories. We can all learn from her.

Many women think about AIDS every day and wish they didn't have to. Before starting this book, AIDS was part of my life. As described in chapter 2, it began with the death of my friend Sebastian, three years ago. What an incredible shock to realize that this disease was real and not just something one reads about in the papers. I lost one of my best friends to AIDS. In all my life, Sebastian's death was the most difficult and painful event I have ever experienced. I have known others since who have died from AIDS-related causes, as have other women. Counselors can benefit by being aware of the personal tragedies that women face as a result of AIDS.

After Sebastian's death, I had to find out more about AIDS. I attended AIDS seminars and workshops to learn all I could about the disease. Today, I give presentations, lectures, and workshops to people who want to learn about AIDS. Counselors also have the option of learning more about AIDS so they can be more effective when helping the victims.

Today, I have two gay friends who may very well be infected with the AIDS virus. They are too scared to be tested; they don't want to know. They are not doing anything to spread the disease, if they should have it.

They have been in a monogamous relationship for four years, but who is to say they didn't contract the AIDS virus five years ago? It's possible, even likely, depending on how sexually active they were. They don't have sex anymore because they're afraid of the possibility of spreading the disease should one or both of them be infected.

They have lost at least twenty-five close friends to AIDS. Half their life is spent in hospitals, saying good-bye to dying friends. But, they persevere and manage to laugh and live their lives to the fullest.

Counselors can take courage and inspiration from these two and use it to provide support and strength to the women they help, who may have similar fears and situations.

Personal Relationships

Many women consider themselves lucky to be in a monogamous relationship. They feel safe and don't consider themselves at risk for getting AIDS. If a woman has never received a blood transfusion or has never been an IV drug user, she may feel safe. This doesn't mean that women cannot empathize with people who are looking for relationships, as revealed by conversations to follow.

On the other hand, there are times when women may be obsessed with the idea that they have AIDS. Every cold evokes, 'Is it PCP?' Any bump, rash, or pimple takes on the proportions of Kaposi's sarcoma. A headache becomes cryptococcal meningitis.

In all probability, these fears come from past encounters with a previous sexual partner whose background didn't seem of import at the time. The odds are actually very low for contracting AIDS from a heterosexual relationship that occurred several years ago (see chapter 4 for further discussion and statistics in regard to heterosexual AIDS transmission).

Recently, I had a conversation with a friend who was interviewed for this book. Although she would like to, she is not in a relationship, having some real concerns about AIDS. She is also the mother of a twenty-two-year-old daughter, which is another source of worry in regard to AIDS. During our conversation, the feminine side of AIDS difficulties in relationships was discussed. This perspective is important for counselors to be aware of when they are helping women.

T: "The relationship with a man to me seems to go beyond the fear of catching AIDS. I'm not a practical person. I think about hurting the other person. To think of saying to some man that I feel close to, 'Excuse me, but do you think you might have AIDS?' I don't know how I could do that, which is ridiculous because it's a question of your own life.

"I think it would depend on where I was. For example, I'm in New York now where AIDS is very prevalent. I don't think I would begin a relationship here. I would be very careful not to.

"However, if I were somewhere else, . . . I could care about someone very quickly, but I'm not the kind of person to be with someone just to be with them. There would have to be something very special about the person. But when there's someone special then it's hard for me to hurt the person. And to me, asking a man if he has AIDS would hurt him.

"If it were the other way around and a man said to me, 'Look, I really like you and I want to be with you, but you might have AIDS so will you please go and find out.' I would say, 'Never mind!' I would feel frozen, 'Okay, let's please not talk about this anymore.' That's ridiculous because AIDS is a very real thing, but I would feel insulted. I don't know if I could deal with that with somebody. Either I wouldn't get into it or I would feel enough that if I did, I wouldn't approach the topic of AIDS.

"If circumstances were the same and you met someone you cared about could you say to that person, 'Do you have AIDS?' What would you say?"

B: "I don't know. I'm real glad that I'm not in that position now."

T: "I'm worried about that (AIDS). A man could say, 'Don't worry about it,' period, and what do you do, keep scratching? It's taken away all the spontaneous romance, and if you're a romanticist, how do you broach the subject without ruining the relationship? I still get hung up about how to say to some man, 'Do you have AIDS?' without hurting them or taking away their dignity or self-respect."

B: "All right, so AIDS is a sexually transmitted disease. There is that stigma, but it is possible that a man could have gotten it through blood transfusions before the blood was screened. It doesn't mean that he necessarily got it through promiscuous sex or drugs. AIDS doesn't have to have that stigma; that negative connotation. The connotation is bad enough that it's a horrible, fatal disease."

T: "I know that if a man got AIDS it doesn't have to be that he was incredibly promiscuous. It could just be that he was with the wrong person once. It might be as simple as that. He went out one night . . . had a few drinks . . . he was lonely, and went home with a woman. He spent one night with her and that was it. A man could say that to you.

"And what if your partner found out that somebody he had a previous relationship with, had AIDS? And he has no intention of going for the test. He says, 'Whatever the

case may be, we've been together and we're in this together.'
How would you feel? Because if you're HIV infected, you
could be in an unknowing state for years."

B: "I know that's a possibility and one that I don't want
to deal with. I hope it never happens because if it does, I
don't know how I would handle it. It's also possible that
someone I was with before this relationship has AIDS. Ultimately, it doesn't matter where the blame is placed."

T: "There are different kinds of people. I, for one,
wouldn't go for testing. I even put off going to the doctor
or the dentist.

"What if I have a relationship with someone and it ends?
The person leaves. Am I free to start a new relationship
or do I have to think about what happened before? And
if I wanted to start a new relationship, asking about AIDS
could ruin it before it has a chance to begin. The man could
say to you, 'If that's the way it is, there are others who are
not going to ask me. You're either with me or you're not.'
There are some men who won't allow a woman to ask
questions like that.

"The men that are exciting to me are like this. They are
strong men who will not put up with questions from a
woman about AIDS. Where can the relationship go if the
guy refuses to deal with your concerns about AIDS?

"Even suppose that a man or a woman knows that he or
she is a carrier. Do you think they're going to stop having
relationships with people? Maybe they really don't want to,
but it happens. At a party, after a few drinks, and you
might meet someone. The opportunity comes up for a relationship. You're both very attracted to each other. Are
you going to say you can't be with this person because you
have AIDS?"

B: "I would hope that if I was an HIV carrier and knew
about it, that I would not put myself in a position to infect

someone else. First of all, I would be so horrified that I wouldn't want to see anybody, let alone put myself in a position of meeting someone."

T: "That's you, you have a lot of awareness and ideals. Let's take a different woman. She's angry and feeling sorry for herself. She meets a man and the opportunity is there. Do you think she would step back and do the right thing?

"That's why I think AIDS is so prevalent. People are so human! If a person tests positive for HIV is he or she going to turn away from life? Maybe, depending on circumstances. Is it really worth it to know if you are infected, or is it better not to know? You might turn away, but can you altogether turn away? You might be careful anyway because you're that type of person, but can you turn away from life completely?"

This dialogue shows the different feelings women may experience about relationships and how they might approach the issue of AIDS with a potential partner. In the case of T., relationships are avoided altogether.

Information for counselors in regard to women's feelings about AIDS testing is presented in the following chapter.

8

Women's Concerns about AIDS Testing

I thought it important to review women's ideas about AIDS testing, both mandatory and in general, because, to date, the topic is brought up in many counseling sessions with women and is also a touchy issue that may involve violations of constitutional rights, as well as legal and ethical implications. Prejudice and discrimination are often the outcome for a person who tests positive for AIDS. Insurance companies don't want to grant medical or life insurance to someone with AIDS.

Confidentiality is a concern for both the person who has AIDS and for the doctor or psychologist who has this person as a patient. If it is not certain whether the person with AIDS will endanger his or her sexual partner, is it ethical for the doctor or psychologist to intervene? While the Tarasoff decision mandates therapists to report a serious threat made by a client toward an intended victim, no guideline yet exists for AIDS, though undoubtedly this will be debated in the courts. People with AIDS can be discriminated against by employers, landlords, insurance companies, and the medical profession, all who may be frightened of contracting the disease.

There is still so much fear and misunderstanding about the disease that the above-mentioned difficulties are far too common. These problems perpetuate the tragedy of AIDS. Not only is one likely to die, but before one does, all aspects of one's life are undermined in such negative ways as to promote isolation and complete loss of support and self-esteem. All of this can come about from misuse of HIV testing.

I also asked the women who had been tested for AIDS to share their experience. I myself have not been tested even though there are times when I am convinced that I have AIDS! I hate to have my blood drawn, so much so that it almost prevented me from getting married because I was afraid to have the blood test! I am a coward but there are several women braver than I, whose feelings about testing are as follows:

Liz, nurse and mother: "I work with many AIDS patients and have for five years. In the beginning when first working with people who had AIDS, I thought that I was being constantly exposed. It was very scary and I often questioned my ability to do my job. As a nurse you are constantly exposed to blood and other body fluids. Now, I'm more comfortable with the risks I take and certainly use extra caution when the likelihood of exposure occurs. I'm very careful with needles when drawing blood because that is a likely way to get the disease—from a needle stick.

"Being a nurse has made me part of an ongoing health-worker study where we are all tested for AIDS antibodies on a regular basis. I have been tested about six times during the past few years and my results have always been negative. Aside from finding out if AIDS can be transmitted in other ways than currently believed, the testing helps me become more reassured that AIDS is not so easy to get. It has also helped me to be more comfortable and less afraid when working with someone who has AIDS.

"The first time I was tested, I was very frightened. I was sure my results would be positive! Now, the testing doesn't scare me any longer. I know what to expect and know that so far, I haven't been careless.

"I also have empathy for those who are not nurses or health-care workers that go for testing. Although I am a firm believer in testing, if you are tested through the public-health system, the results can take several weeks. I think this is discouraging to many people who may have been more likely to have testing on the spur of the moment if they could have results in a few days. And how about the junkie who can't think ahead a day at a time? I think there should be a special set-up for drug users in regard to testing and fast results. If you go to your private doctor, you can get test results in a few days, but how many junkies go to private doctors? For me, this is a main area of concern. We can't stop spreading AIDS until each of us knows if we have it or not."

Question: Do you think you've been exposed to the AIDS virus? If so, have you been tested?

Michelle: "I've stopped working as a nurse for three years now. Before I stopped, there was nobody in the hospital that had AIDS. We didn't protect ourselves unless we knew someone had a specific illness. AIDS wasn't truly a consideration at that point. I would start IVs, give resuscitation, and inevitably had bodily fluid contact from patients. I didn't have myself tested; never considered it.

"Recently, my husband and I were asked to donate blood. My husband donates once a year but I have never gotten around to give it. This was so much on my mind and I wasn't feeling great just before we had to go. I ended up not going again but my husband did. He returned with a list of information stating that the blood was tested for the AIDS virus. I was both relieved and very nervous at the same time. I assume that within three weeks he will be notified if he tested positive for the AIDS antibodies. I feel a little more comfortable. If he doesn't have it, I probably don't either.

"Sometimes I worry when I think back to Thanksgiving,

1983. I was pregnant and my son and husband went to relatives. I stayed in the area because I had to work; I was a nurse at the time. I went to a friend's for dinner and the person who was cooking was a gay man in his early thirties. He had been sick off and on for a while. AIDS was not really epidemic at that point (or at least I didn't believe so).

"I was smoking cigarettes at that time and I remember taking drags from his cigarette. He was sick and as a matter of fact, during dinner he had to go and lie down.

"About a week later he was much sicker and my girlfriend called asking me what to do for him. Should she make him go to a doctor or the hospital? I recommended a few doctors, and they said to the man, 'Absolutely not. You don't have AIDS.'

"At that point, I didn't want to be too physically close to him because I was pregnant and worried I might pick up something. I really didn't know what was wrong with him.

"He continued to go to doctors who again told him that he didn't have AIDS. When I think back he had all the AIDS symptoms: coughing, drastic weight loss, fever, cyanotic (poor color, ashen complexion).

"Finally he was put in an ambulance (on oxygen) to New York City where he was immediately diagnosed with AIDS. Six weeks later, he was dead.

"So, have I been exposed? I guess as much as I can be without blood to blood, body fluid exchange. It's difficult as a nurse in the emergency room to avoid certain situations that might infect you. Your main concern is to save a life, not worry about your own. Unfortunately, I would have to reconsider nursing if I decided to ride an ambulance again."

Michelle's concerns are shared by many nurses and doctors. I have heard stories of doctors and nurses outright refusing to treat AIDS patients because they are so fright-ened of contracting the disease. Many nurses and doctors get tested for AIDS antibodies on a regular basis as a safeguard and as part of ongoing research of health-care workers.

Patricia, social worker, on testing:
"I feel testing is a very 'touchy' situation. Especially, with regard to the anonymity of the test results. The smaller the metropolitan area you live in the more people are likely to 'know your business.' Just the fact that you were con-cerned enough to be tested implies that you might think you have the disease. Good gossip in small towns. Where I live if I wanted to be guaranteed anonymous test results, I would have to go to a clinic in New York City. If you're not tested by a clinic and you are tested by a regular phy-sician, everything is on file. I think the public would be very surprised at how easy it is to obtain information which is thought to be 'private.' The disease has a great stigma attached to it and you could always test false positive for the antibodies.

"In my job I work with a high-risk group; IV drug users and their children. If I tested false positive for AIDS and was asymptomatic, the agency I work for would let me go (illegal discrimination, but a reality).

"I don't think testing should be mandatory. There is so much fear about the disease and now almost an 'AIDS panic.' I can see the government putting people who tested positive for the disease under quarantine. Instead of leper colonies; AIDS colonies. I really feel mandatory testing would be against human rights.

"I haven't been tested for the disease, but have given it serious thought. For now, I don't want to know. For me, the fear of not knowing is easier to live with than knowing if I have the disease. I'm not having sex with anyone, so I know I'm not spreading or contracting the disease. My conscience is clear."

Alice, mother and social worker who had an AIDS test:
"I recently found out that a friend of mine, a woman, has AIDS. She is still working and doesn't look sick. She just doesn't look like what I'd expect somebody who has AIDS to look like. It shook me up very badly. I thought that if she has AIDS, I could have AIDS. I went through days of torment about it because it had occurred to me even before my friend got sick, that I should have the test, but I denied it, squelched it.

"I came to what I felt was a real moral dilemma. For example, what if I was one of the carriers of the disease who never got sick but had the virus? It would be horrible to know but at the same time, it would be more horrible to unknowingly infect your children or someone you might have an intimate relationship with.

"It was really strange to have these thoughts because I'm not a martyr or a saint. I've never been the most moralistic person although I am to a certain degree. I just do things I don't think I should do and then feel guilty afterward.

"In this sense it was an amazing thing for me to have to face it. No, I don't want to know that I have AIDS, I don't want to know that, I don't want to be freaked out of my mind.

"I would be crazed if I had AIDS but I felt it was absolutely necessary for me to be tested. In this case, being crazed would be the lesser of two wrongs. I just told a friend that I wanted it on my gravestone that I died with moral conviction!

"For two days I was sure that I had AIDS. After I had the test—going through the test! First of all. I'm angry that I went alone. I sometimes forget how fragile I am and I put myself in this outrageous situation. I went to my doctor and he counseled me for a half an hour. Then I had to go to the lab to have the actual test. I handed the girl the piece of paper that says AIDS test and she gave me a look like she's not real thrilled, so I had to say, 'My doctor thinks it's ridiculous that I'm having this test,' because she is wearing a look of total fear. She does not want to do this test on me.

"After all, look what she does for a living every day. She told me she had the AIDS test herself after I told her it wasn't likely that I had it. She became a little more relaxed but I was very uptight because I felt like I was taking care of her and it should have been the other way around.

"After the test, I returned to my doctor who gave me a mailing kit and number to send in my blood for anonymity. Then, I had to take the kit to the post office to mail it.

"You won't believe what happened at the post office! It's like something out of a Woody Allen movie. I'm standing in line with this AIDS kit in my hand and I'm totally freaked out because I've been under so much stress with my friend who has AIDS, and my thinking that I have it too. I glanced down thinking, 'Whose going to know what this is—no one.' I look up and there stands a doctor who I have slept with! I thought, how hysterical! Here stands the only person who might know what this kit is and I had slept with him! I should have said, 'Have a nice weekend! Life is short!' "

At the time of Alice's interview, she did not know the test results. I have spoken to her since, and am happy to report that the results are negative. Alice has brought up some sensitive issues for those of you who may be considering testing or suggesting testing to someone else. If one is nervous about having the test, as most people would be, it's a good idea to bring a friend for emotional support. Alice regrets going alone because it was a trying experience. If she had a friend with her, she may have been able to laugh off the uncomfortable attitude presented by the lab assistant.

Kathy, a teacher, has ideas on testing. "Mandatory testing is kind of a Nazi attitude. We are supposed to be free in this country. People who suspect that they have AIDS take responsibility for themselves, get tested on their own, and not transmit the disease. That's part of what I believe this disease is about. People who have had contact, promiscuous sexual contact, should be tested on their own."

Harriet Barrett, on testing. "Scary, knowing the way people are, mandatory testing could be a weapon. That's my biggest fear, to have one more group that we can hate, like the Nazis. The Jews had to wear a yellow star to distinguish them. For some reason I'm frightened of that aspect because if you have AIDS, you'll know it, and a lot of people are fearful.

"What's the good of knowing you have AIDS until the symptoms actually appear? I don't see what benefit it is to people. I have a fear of that power being used incorrectly. My fear is greater than the knowledge of a person having it."

Question: What if you were out looking for a relationship? How do you feel about testing in this case?

Harriet: "No, I've thought about that and I'm grateful I'm not single. I'm frightened for my kids. I've asked lots of friends how they handle it, and the answers I was most comfortable with were the ones that didn't get a prospective partner up against the wall with a test. Instead of going straight to bed, the relationship would develop slowly at first until it became strong. Finally, a discussion of pasts and life-styles and then use condoms. That's just how I relate to relationships.

"Mandatory testing I've never been into or signing papers about whose money is whose before you marry. Even though AIDS is more life and death than economics, somehow, that's how I feel I'd have to cope.

"With me, I'd only have a test if I felt symptomatic because what is the good of knowing, that means nothing except to get me more neurotic."

Question: Do you feel you've been exposed to the AIDS virus?

Harriet: "I don't know. It's been so many years. Theoretically from what they've said, no, but if in fact AIDS is a time bomb, who knows? Look at our past. We were hippies and all of us said, 'Look what we came through and we made it.' Well, maybe we haven't made it, but you can die crossing the street, too. I look both ways, therefore, I would also use condoms.

"I haven't been tested, even with the death of a friend to AIDS, not wearing gloves when the aides at the hospital insisted. I immediately did think that I was covered with mosquito bites which were open. I got scared and then put it aside. I think either because I didn't want to cope with it or I just don't believe it's really possible to get infected in that way.

"And sure, a girl can get pregnant the first time ever with somebody—that's more a shot in the dark (pardon the pun!) but usually one needs more exposure both for pregnancy and AIDS. I don't have a life-style that leaves me open to that much exposure."

Betty, teacher, on testing. "My biggest fear with the notion of mandatory testing is the violation of basic human rights. I don't think people should be tested for AIDS on the job. How can that information remain confidential? Someone has to know about it, personnel for example. Also, do some employers make people leave their jobs if they test positive for the AIDS virus? If someone with AIDS is able to work, he or she should be allowed to do so unless, of course, he or she becomes too ill to continue. Then, they should leave on their own cognizance.

"How can people be tested before becoming employed? Does that mean that all the people who have been employed for say ten or fifteen years have to be tested also? What an incredible violation of one's privacy.

"On children with AIDS in school—look at the horrible reaction of townspeople who burned the house of the three hemophiliac brothers who had AIDS. Since I am a teacher in the public-school system, I realize the incredible fears that some parents have. I know that some children with AIDS are kept from attending school. Again, this is a complete panic reaction because if AIDS is not spread through casual contact, there theoretically should be no fear of infection to others. I think children with AIDS should be allowed to continue school as long as they are well enough to do so.

"In regard to testing in conjunction with marriage (marriage license) I think it's a good idea. I don't think it will completely stop the spread of AIDS but it could be crucial to those individuals who want to have children. I realize that many children are born outside of marriage and testing won't help in these cases. But for the couples who get married and want a family, I think AIDS testing is important. Both partners should know beforehand if either has AIDS. They still may want to get married but I don't think they should have children. From what I understand the chances of a baby being born with the AIDS virus if the mother is infected is greater than fifty percent. As of now, there is no hope for babies who contract AIDS so it's a terribly unfair thing to inflict on an unborn child. I don't know how abortions could be mandated in these cases but hopefully, most parents would make the proper decision."

The above women's responses to testing were most representative of all the women interviewed. Recognizing these areas will help counselors talk to women about the highly emotionally charged concept about AIDS testing. Major concerns were voiced in regard to the number of infants being born HIV positive. Many women believe that testing in conjunction with marriage licenses may be one way in which to cut back on these tragic numbers of babies born of infected mothers. On the other hand, HIV testing before marriage will do little to help babies born outside of wedlock, which I assume may sometimes be the case with parents who are IV drug abusers. My feeling is that testing, in conjunction with education through drug rehabilitation programs, may be more effective than testing by itself. Unfortunately, there are not enough rehabilitation programs to accommodate the IV drug users who are most at risk for contracting AIDS. Hopefully, more monies will be put toward expansion of these critical programs in the immediate future.

The other major testing concern expressed by women in these pages is the terrible recrimination that can result from mandatory testing; ultimately, the violation of human rights. Women are likening mandatory testing to Nazi Germany and the horrors of the Holocaust that resulted. In this area, I agree. I have seen terrible prejudice and discrimination in only the past four years, which has been born out of fear of AIDS. Certainly, AIDS is something to be afraid of, but with education supposedly comes knowledge and understanding. For some, this is true, but not for all. This is simply the differences of human nature and cannot be changed.

But for those who can overcome their fear and go on to help—this is where hope of conquering AIDS, or at least getting through the crisis, lies.

The following chapter focuses on women and their concerns and opinions on the media coverage in regard to AIDS.

9

Women and the Media

Whatever one believes as truth, the media have played a tremendous role in the AIDS epidemic. I wanted to see how women responded to the media's involvement with AIDS so they were asked to share their opinions, which are presented later in the chapter.

The media are an important influence on how people view events, issues, and AIDS. Without the media people would be virtually "in the dark" about important issues, having no frame of reference, nothing to compare, no information, and no feedback, which results in ignorance. But, it is important how the media present the facts, particularly in regard to a tragic event such as AIDS—a new disease . . . a new epidemic . . . a new plague. It is a powerful tool that can influence and color the way in which people perceive and understand, for example, AIDS. Most people believe what they see on TV, hear on the radio, and read in the news.

People have many choices in regard to which newspaper or magazine they will read, i.e., the *New York Times* or the *New York Post, Newsweek,* or *People.* People make media choices that fit their personality, intellect, or mood. Although people do have certain options, the media must assume the responsibility of presenting the facts in a timely manner.

Randy Shilts, in his book *And the Band Played On,* feels that media were irresponsible in their delay of concern and coverage about AIDS, resulting in a precious loss of time that delayed critical research, which allowed the epidemic its fatal foothold in this country. Shilts believes that because AIDS initially infected the male homosexual population, the media were reticent to become involved with this touchy, political subject.

Today, the AIDS epidemic has gone beyond the homosexual population. Heterosexuals, women, and babies are infected, and the gay percentage has dropped from 71 percent in 1985 to 38 percent in 1987 (*New York Times*, December 13, 1987). Shilts, among others, feels that the media are largely to blame for the huge numbers of people infected with HIV, because their lack of initial coverage delayed prevention tactics that may at least have put a halt to the continued spread of the disease.

My initial reaction to the media's coverage of AIDS was one of shock, occurring in conjunction with the death of my friend, Sebastian, who died of an AIDS-related infection in 1985. I realized I hadn't really heard that much about AIDS. I certainly didn't think that AIDS could affect me. Sebastian's death brought the disease into my life, and I took it upon myself to learn about it. Usually, I'm an avid reader; I listen to the news and attempt to keep informed, therefore, if the media had adequately covered the reality of AIDS, I certainly would have known about it.

Prior to 1985, I remember reading about AIDS in a 1983 issue of *Science* magazine. The article discussed the concerns of CDC doctors and researchers who were attempting to find a cause and treatment for the disease that had infected gay men (particularly in the San Francisco area), Haitians, IV drug users and their sexual partners, hemophiliacs, and children. Out of 891 of the AIDS cases, 333 had died. The researchers thought that AIDS could be transmitted through blood products, and had feared that the disease could spread to many, through blood-bank supplies used in transfusions, etc. *Two years* after this article appeared in *Science,* the blood banks employed screening procedures to detect the HIV virus. I am convinced that many people would have avoided contracting the disease if the blood had been screened earlier.

This irresponsibility on the part of the media (lack of adequate AIDS coverage) certainly contributed to the two-year delay in blood-bank screening for AIDS.

The *Science* article impressed me and was an excellent source of current information on AIDS; however, how many people read *Science* magazine? My guess is that fewer people read *Science* magazine than, for example, read *People* magazine. If *Science* had such grave concerns and fears about the disease, why was it not taken up in a wider sense by the media? I think this contributed to my increased apathy about AIDS until Sebastian died. Also, I did not fit into the group of people who were dying so I didn't think I would be affected. Even though I had homosexual friends, the gay men I knew did not live in San Franciso where the disease seemed more prevalent. Therefore, physical location was another factor that decreased my concern of being directly affected by the disease. I certainly felt empathy and concern for the people who were infected; I don't mean to appear cold-blooded and uncaring, but all of the media's disconcern for AIDS prior to 1985 contributed to my feeling removed from the reality of the disease.

Rock Hudson's death in October 1985 brought AIDS to the media forefront where it has remained to date. Unfortunately, I feel that many needless deaths may have been prevented if the media had jumped in sooner. At this time, most women were not aware that AIDS would become a direct threat to them. Not only would their sons, husbands, and lovers possibly become infected, but they could as well.

Following, are several women's responses to the question, "What do you feel about the media's coverage of AIDS? Has it been underemphasized or overemphasized?"

Denise, book illustrator and San Francisco resident:
"I think AIDS information has been too late in coming. The media seem to emphasize the negative aspects about homosexuality. It's almost as if the media says, 'Don't worry if you are not a homosexual.' I resent the lack of coverage of the positive aspects of the gay culture such as the gay march, gay rights, and the fight and courage it took to get there. What about gay contributions to society, particularly in the arts? I also don't know how much the media holds back, how biased it is. In my world, homosexuality is the norm rather than the oddity. The media is stressing so much about AIDS and homosexuality that people are going to start to believe it isn't all right to be gay anymore. The country will regress to the homophobic state it was in just a few short years ago. I am saddened to think a setback like this might happen.

"Finally, I would like to see a push for educational tactics rather than scare tactics. I don't believe the promotion of hysteria will help fight AIDS."

Liz, registered nurse, mother, and San Francisco resident:
"I feel the media coverage has been definitely underestimated. *Everyone* has the right to know the facts. More 'scare' should be put into the public's mind. Not so much a scare but an awareness and factual understanding of AIDS must be relayed across the world.

"Although media coverage was initially underestimated, it is now distorted. Too much focus is still on homosexuals and drug users with little emphasis on the fact that anyone can get AIDS. I think that once the media can appeal to people's humanity, it will be doing its best to help deal with the disease.

"As a Latin woman, I am frightened at the disproportionate impact of AIDS on minorities. The media continue to neglect the devastation to these groups and I would like to see a positive push toward support of these people. The media can be responsible and unbiased toward all people regardless of color or beliefs. I don't think they have been up to this point. As a nurse, I've lived with this epidemic for more than five years and have seen the reality of the devastation. Now, more than ever, it's up to the media to give us a fair, real picture of this terrible disease. I still talk to many people who don't seem affected and don't even take AIDS seriously. Some of these people actually think that one day they will read the paper and all mention of AIDS will have disappeared. I recently talked to someone who said, 'What happened to herpes or Legionnaire's Disease? I never read a word about them anymore. Maybe AIDS will disappear just like those illnesses did.' I can't believe that any halfway intelligent human being who reads or watches television thinks that AIDS is just going to disappear. The media can make a difference to people who have this false idea."

Liz's concerns about the media's effect on the population in regard to AIDS being viewed as a disease likened to herpes is reiterated in a recent conversation I had with my father who lives in a rural area in upstate New York, six hours north of New York City. He is an intelligent man who takes a great interest in people. He keeps up with media world events by means of radio, television, and magazines/newspapers. He is aware of AIDS and keeps up with current facts on the topic. Our conversation went like this. Would-be counselors take heed!

B: "What are your feelings and concerns about AIDS? I know you read about it. I am affected by it every day and it's pretty scary. How are you affected?"

D: "Well, I know you had a hard time when your friend died. I didn't know him but I know how special he was to you. As far as I realize, I don't know anyone who has AIDS. I don't even know any homosexuals, at least none that I'm aware of."

B: "But anyone can get AIDS, not just homosexuals. As a matter of fact, the homosexual population has dropped by more than half in regard to risk groups. Now, IV drug abusers and their sexual partners are more at risk. Babies are being born with AIDS through their infected mothers. Look at the recent state study where one in sixty-one babies born in New York City tested HIV positive. Women can get and transmit AIDS also."

D: "I do hear about all this but somehow I have the feeling that one day AIDS won't be in the news anymore. It will just disappear like Legionnaires' disease or the swine flu. I guess since I don't have any direct involvement at this time, AIDS seems removed, more of an unreality. I don't mean to sound cold-blooded; it sure is a terrible disease and I feel for those who get it."

B: "What about your granddaughter? Don't you think she could get it if she isn't careful? Do you have any fear for her?"

D: "I never thought about her being at risk for getting AIDS. I guess she could get it if she's not cautious. Now, I'll worry about her! It never crossed my mind until now."

Again, this conversation supports the fact that people who do not know anyone with AIDS tend to feel removed from the reality of the tragedy. Until the majority of the people are directly affected AIDS will not be a major issue or concern for these people. I too believe that the day will come when, unfortunately, everyone will be touched by AIDS. People who attempt to counsel and assist others about AIDS should be aware that this is a common reaction.

Kathy, in response to the AIDS media coverage: "I think the media has covered AIDS unjustly from a sensationalism standpoint in terms of the gay population. My friend, Father M., told me that there were just as many straight people as gay people coming into Bellevue Hospital each week with AIDS. It is not just a gay disease and if the figures had been published, people would panic to realize how many people were actually developing the disease. I learned about this several years ago. I feel the coverage towards the gay people has basically been unjust and unfair. It seems the media were trying to develop homophobia amongst everyone in the world."

Homophobia is a concern of many, and AIDS counselors will eventually be asked to help and to listen to other's fears on this subject. Even today, homophobia is a central issue regarding AIDS.

Barbara, on the media: "I think AIDS is covered a lot lately. Trying to let people know that even though it is a horrible disease, just because someone has it they shouldn't be avoided, i.e., shaking hands, going to school with an AIDS person, etc.

"I thought AIDS was covered properly in the beginning and there was a panic factor involved which I believed was good, only in regard to the seriousness and horror of the reality of the disease.

"Sometimes today, I feel that the media is going in the opposite direction, underplaying AIDS to stop panic. I hope the estimates are not as bad as I think they're going to be.

"In *Time* I read about two strains of HIV that are coming out of Africa. Somebody could have symptoms, get tested for HIV-1 and have negative results when, in fact, they have the HIV-2 strain which cannot be detected by screening methods that are used in this country. That's a concern of mine."

Patricia, on the media: "I think media hype is just that, 'media hype.'

"AIDS is serious, of course, it's very serious. I think that the media have been downplaying AIDS lately. It's a two-sided issue ... people need to know, need to be well-informed and educated, but on the other hand, people don't need to be put in a panic.

"Even after attending an AIDS workshop sponsored by the Department of Health, I didn't learn concrete answers. There are still too many unknowns about the nature of the disease itself. There's still no cure for cancer and it's been around a lot longer than AIDS. Of course, you can't give anyone cancer if you have it.

"I listened to the surgeon general talking about a cure for AIDS. He compared it to hepatitis B, which is also contagious and deadly. It took nineteen years to find a cure for hepatitis. He said that was easy compared to finding a cure for AIDS. But then, who knows, maybe a cure for AIDS is right around the corner! I hope so."

Alice, on the media: "I think the media coverage is about right. It was more scandalous and titillating at first, but it drew attention that way. Maybe it wasn't as serious or profound as it should have been. I do think that when AIDS was considered mostly a gay problem, it didn't get enough attention. Thank God for Rock Hudson.

"Now, everytime I pick up a magazine or newspaper, there is something about AIDS. That's not overdoing it. Despite the media, I think there are still so many of us walking around denying AIDS exists. It's a horrible disease and none of us really want to face it."

Michelle, on the media: "One of the serious misrepresentations of the media is that on any television show or movie you see people hugging, kissing, and in bed together, and no use or mention of condoms. I watched *Broadcast News* the other night and the woman put a pack of condoms in her purse. It was the first time I had seen condoms displayed in any movie.

"The media, especially because teenagers get so much information from it, should think more about AIDS, talking about condoms when sexuality is part of the program.

"When I was a teenager it was horrifying to even think about condoms, and that was for birth control. It was embarrassing. I never mentioned condoms and very few friends did either. But this is more serious than birth control. This is life and death. It has to become much more matter-of-fact so people become more comfortable with the topic [condoms]."

The following response to the media question presents an interesting interaction between mother and teenage son. Parents who might speak to their children about AIDS may find this helpful and enlightening.

Harriet, on the media: "AIDS is finally out there a lot now so people have to hear it. It's almost like the Vietnamese War which was on so often it was nonreal. I didn't realize how unreal it was until I approached the kids with a discussion about AIDS. I thought, there is such a blitz that people have to hear it. I don't need to say a word to the kids who listen to the advertising . . . condoms, etc.

"Only to approach my fourteen-year-old son about working with a friend of ours who has AIDS. I was sure that he had learned a lot about the topic through television advertising. I asked, 'What do you know about AIDS?' And I realized he saw the ads on television as just another cartoon."

D (son): "I don't know."

H: "Well, what are you watching? What is a condom? What is it about?"

D: "I don't understand what I see. I haven't really paid attention."

Schools have the opportunity to provide one-on-one discussion in regard to AIDS. Kids are forced to listen and interact, so they'll have to play dumb and say, 'I don't know what you're talking about. What does that mean?' Finally, the discussion results.

"That's how I correlate AIDS to the Vietnam War coverage. Bloodshed was no big thing. We saw it every night on the news.

"I don't know what the solution is but I don't think the media output is working yet. I am glad it's out there. Anything is better than the prehistoric state we were in, but we're not even halfway there."

Harriet's concerns are to be noted because despite the blitz of information on television, the AIDS messages are going over the heads of the children. Hearing so much about it, they tune out, it becomes not real. Parents need to be aware of this situation, not taking for granted that their children are getting enough information and education through the media. (See chapter on "Children and AIDS" for age-appropriate dialogue on the subject.)

Many women agree that the media coverage of AIDS has been inadequate and in certain instances, unrealistic (in regard to condoms, for example). It is women who have noticed that their children are not understanding AIDS media messages. Counselors can learn from women's insight into these issues to better understand how to help them in regard to AIDS.

Women talking to children about AIDS is presented in the next chapter. Counselors can also learn how to help women talk to their children.

10

Women Talking to Children about AIDS

Many women will want guidelines on talking to their children about AIDS. One basic theme is that children think differently than adults. As an adult, it is not beneficial to impose adult logic on a child. Once we understand how a child thinks at different developmental stages, we can be successful in communicating with them. Since the topic of AIDS involves a great deal of understanding about sexuality, it is important to know how to appropriately talk to children of different ages about this sensitive issue. My intent is to provide some guidelines on how to talk to children of all ages about AIDS. Following is a basic exploration of childhood stages: how they see the world, how they think, what they may be capable of understanding as adults, and how adults may attempt to listen and communicate with them. Perhaps this will be a useful framework for counselors who work with women.

Toddlers (Birth to Three)

Babies and toddlers need the security that love and warmth of the home environment can bring. Therefore, it is not appropriate to frighten children with something (AIDS) they are not yet able to understand. Children need the security of the first three years so that they may gain strength and confidence to deal with life's problems as they grow older.

The Magic Years: Three to Six

During this period, children learn there is a world larger than their immediate family. They are involved with play, fantasy, and discovery, and learn to feel responsible for the belief that their thoughts can cause an event to happen. For example, it is common for many children to become angry with the parents they have such a close bond with. It is not uncommon for a child to say, "I hate you!" to his or her parent. If the parent were to leave during or shortly after this episode the child is likely to attribute the desertion to his or her anger.

I remember an incident when I was five years old. My parents went out for the evening, leaving me with a baby-sitter who I was not that familiar with. Since my parents didn't go out often, this was an unusual occurrence for me. My mother put me to bed before she left, telling me not to get out of bed without first asking the sitter, and only for a good reason. Otherwise, I was to go to sleep for the night. Of course, I had a difficult time falling asleep and decided I needed a drink of water. I called to the sitter several times to ask if I could get out of bed to get a drink. She didn't respond. I called again even louder. Finally, I was screaming for a drink of water. It seemed impossible to me that she couldn't hear. I became angry, particularly at my parents who left me with someone who was so insensitive. I finally stopped shouting because it got me nowhere but I was fuming at my parents. As the evening wore on, I became frightened, thinking my parents would never return home, because I had misbehaved. Needless to say, they did come home but I was convinced they wouldn't because of my behavior.

Magic-years children are beginning to learn to control their impulses and emotions. Their feelings can sometimes appear frightening. They are becoming exposed to violence via television and scary fairy tales that are upsetting and can cause nightmares.

Again, drawing from my own experience, I remember having recurring nightmares during this age span, about wolves chasing me through the woods at night. I would awake and run into my parents' bedroom, trying to climb into their bed for comfort. I believe these dreams stemmed from seeing photographs of a friend of my father's who went hunting for wolves. In the picture he is standing beside two dead wolves that he had killed.

During this time frame it would be best to allow children to grow in relative innocence, concentrating on mastering the challenges of their environment before becoming burdened with adult problems. However, it is not always possible to insulate children from the real issues about AIDS that they may hear about on TV or from an adult discussion and want to ask about. For these inquisitive children, adults should be accessible to their questions, to be perceived as someone the child can turn to if troubled, and to assure the child that he or she is loved.

Most important, adults should answer questions about AIDS as reassuringly and positively as possible, redirecting their attention to what people are doing to help, and to focus on positive aspects. If adults project uncertainty and fear, the children will absorb these feelings.

For example, a six-year-old girl overhears two classmates, one of whom says, "I bet you have AIDS. You're gonna die!" She doesn't really know what AIDS is but thinks about it until she gets home when she asks her mother about it.

DAUGHTER: Mommy, what is AIDS? Can people die from it?

MOTHER: What did you hear about AIDS?

DAUGHTER: In school some kids said somebody was gonna die if they had it.

MOTHER: AIDS is a disease that is very hard to get. It's true that some people have it but doctors are working very hard to help people who have it. I don't want you to be scared because you won't get AIDS even if someone we know has it. It's not like a cold that you can catch from somebody.

In summary: when responding to young children's questions and concerns about AIDS, focus on the positive. Try not to project anxiety and fear even though you may be feeling these emotions. Listen carefully and keep your answers direct, simple, and truthful. Young children need to feel safe and loved.

The Middle Years: Six to Twelve

Middle-years children think on a concrete level and are often very direct and blunt in conversation. Adults might view their thoughts as morbid, but this is normal for children of this age. For example, this age period is often the time of a child's first experience attending a wake or funeral of a grandparent or relative. It is not uncommon to hear, "Why is Grandma so cold? Will she rot and only have bones left?" Adults have learned not to mention these thoughts but they can be expected from a child.

As adults, people must learn how to be good listeners and to look for the nonverbal cues that arise in their children's writing, artwork, and play. Be honest and direct in responding to their questions, and when having difficulty answering say, "I don't know. I'll have to find out or look it up for you." Don't force questions but develop a climate where the children feel comfortable asking questions. Remember that truth is less frightening than mystery, and many children have misconceptions about AIDS. Answers to direct questions like, "How do you get AIDS?" "What is AIDS?" or "Why do you die from AIDS?" may give children a more realistic understanding of the issue. Lack of communication can lead to isolation and indifference between family members. A lonely person is not a healthy person. Keep the way open and comfortable for interaction and conversation.

Read and learn about AIDS together with your children and discuss concerns that arise. Admit what you don't know and look it up for further discussion. Be truthful and direct and most of all, provide an environment open to questions from your children. .

Teenagers

Most teenagers are capable of understanding on an adult level, but rapport and trust need to be established before open talk about AIDS concerns progresses. Very often, teenagers look at adults as "know-it-alls" and refuse to open up and interact. We have all listened to the timeworn phrase of, "When I was a boy things were different. I walked five miles through the snow to school every day," etc. I myself groan inwardly when I hear this common saying.

People as adults/parents need to break down this barrier of misunderstanding that leads to no communication. I think that adolescents need to hear that adults don't have all the answers, and that they too need to grope around and find their way at times.

For example, when I talk to kids about AIDS, I always make it a point to share a real experience and to acknowledge that I've have a hard time dealing with AIDS too. Sharing your uncertainty about the disease lends credibility. Show your vulnerability; don't hide it and be looked upon as a rigid know-it-all.

Teenagers' Feelings

People as adults can easily project their own fears and anxiety onto their children. Adults must first acknowledge their fear and put it into perspective so that they don't inadvertently frighten their children. It's okay for adults to appear vulnerable at times but they also need to provide support and security.

To effectively communicate with children about AIDS adults need to be able to:

(1) Face their own fears
(2) Deal with guilt
(3) Say, "I don't know"
(4) Acknowledge their feelings of helplessness
(5) Help children feel safe
(6) Let go of the need to make everything okay
(7) Help children verbalize their feelings
(8) Attempt a normal life despite the reality of AIDS

This sounds like a tall order, but if adults can tackle these issues one by one they may hope to achieve an open line of communication with children. In return, children should be able to express what they don't understand about AIDS.

Some of the teenagers I've talked to have expressed resentment about AIDS interfering with their growing up and sexuality. It's one thing to worry about pregnancy, another to worry about getting a disease that can kill you. I have heard statements like, "Why couldn't we be born in the sixties when it was acceptable to be sexually free and there was no worry of AIDS." It's particularly hard on adolescents who are just beginning to experience sexuality and want to make choices of their own about relationships. AIDS is out there and for those who choose any kind of sexual relationship, it's almost like playing Russian roulette.

On the other hand, many teens are not really worried about AIDS even though they are aware it exists. They feel it won't happen to them, they're invulnerable. For the helper, this presents a large stumbling block to effective communication.

AIDS and Education

As a member of an AIDS committee in the public-school system, I have been aware of the controversy over teaching about AIDS to schoolchildren. The controversy is such that it has interfered with program development in the schools. In order to be realistic, AIDS education must involve talk about death, sex, and morality. Our committee consists of parents, clergy, teachers, and community members who each have differing viewpoints on what is appropriate to teach children.

Some of the varying views and objections to teaching children about AIDS are: "They're too young," "We don't need to scare them and make them anxious," "We don't want to make them frightened of having sex," "It's inappropriate to discuss homosexuality with children," "We can't do anything about it anyway so why bring it up," "People who get AIDS are going to die anyway," and "I want to be the one to teach my children about sexuality and AIDS, it's not appropriate for the school to impose its views on my child."

It is extremely difficult, if not impossible to please everyone but in New York State, schools have been mandated (from the state level) to teach children about AIDS, from kindergarten through high school. The state has issued grade-appropriate guidelines to be loosely used in teaching children. Each school district then has the choice of amending these guidelines to fit what it feels is appropriate for its school, hence, the AIDS committee that makes recommendations to present to the school district for the final program.

This is all well and good but without adequate communication between home and the school, education about AIDS could be self-defeating. AIDS education must breach the possibility of contradiction from the home level. Parents need to be aware and become involved with what is being taught about AIDS in the school. This calls for a much broader program to educate parents as well, which hopefully will result in some consistency for the children.

A concern that I have in regard to AIDS education is that it is extremely important for kids to learn to respect others' viewpoints even as they differ from their own. AIDS involves many controversial issues, i.e., sexuality, drug abuse, homosexuality, and sexually transmitted disease, that certainly can be starting points for prejudice. It would be a positive educational factor to incorporate discussion about people's differing ideas about AIDS, and to learn respect for them.

The most caring outlook about AIDS education was expressed by a mother of a school-age child. "My concern is not that my daughter will get AIDS, but that she should have love, warmth, and compassion for the little kid who comes to school and has it."

Many of the concerns about children and AIDS are discussed by the women interviewed as follows:

Nancy: "I don't think that children who have contracted

the disease should be stigmatized the way they are. These children are really innocents. For example, the incident of the three hemophiliac boys in Florida: the stigma in their town was so great that prejudiced townspeople burned their house down. Ignorance and fear of the disease have paralyzed people.

"Children and adults should be taught that AIDS is a communicable disease but that it's not contagious; that if someone with the disease breathes or sneezes on you, you won't get the disease. Children shouldn't feel frightened that they can easily get the disease.

"Teenagers today are, or at least have been, sexually active at an earlier age. My mother was from the time period that said, 'You shouldn't have sex until you're married, and then, only with that one man.' When I was younger and just beginning to become sexually active, it was socially acceptable to have more than one sexual partner before marriage. You don't hear the word 'virgin' much anymore.

"Life is hard enough when you're an adolescent and you're dealing with the first stirrings of 'sexuality.' My concern for teenagers today is for the child who feels he or she is invulnerable, the teen who says, 'I won't get AIDS, not me!' It's hard to think about mortality, especially when you're a teenager and the whole world is just opening up for you."

Alice, social worker, mother of two teenagers: "Children should be aware that AIDS is here. That it's very, very real. I talked to my daughter and her friends weeks ago after learning that a woman friend of mine had AIDS. My daughter is a little too 'hip,' she misses things sometimes. I said, 'Look, I have a friend who has AIDS; her husband has AIDS. I think that if any of you are having sex, just don't.

"They said that nobody at school has sex with anybody

except the kids at school. I said, 'Oh, come on! First of all, one of those kids from school may have had a blood transfusion. And what about your friends whose parents are IV drug users?'

"I realize that it's unlikely any of these kids have AIDS but not as unlikely as other kids from more rural areas. What about the kids who might get high (drink or smoke) and have sex with an older man? Or what about the kids who visit their separated/divorced parents who live in New York City or some other urban area?

"It's too real. I was sort of relying on the media because my kids are intelligent and aware, until my friend got AIDS. This is not anything to be taken the least bit lightly. I realized the media were not really reaching my kids because they still weren't terribly concerned about the possibility of getting AIDS. I hope that I reached them and made them think more seriously about the possibilities and precautions they should take."

Liz, nurse: "Children should be taught that AIDS isn't easy to get. When it's age-appropriate, kids can be told that it's a sexually transmitted disease that can also be contracted by drug use and sharing needles. Most important, AIDS is nobody's fault; it's a disease. Facts about how you *don't* get it should be stressed. Morality concerning premarital sex and sexual freedom should be taught in the home. Soon children will be the adults and a cure may be in their hands."

Michelle T., nurse, mother of two: "I think that AIDS education for children is very important. Children from very early on are aware of health vs. illness and I think that AIDS, maybe not the actual word to kindergartners, but the idea of communicable diseases should be told to them.

"The fact that AIDS is in the blood—I don't think that method of disease transmission has been known to young children. They know that if you sneeze you should cover your mouth so you don't give someone a cold.

"One of my concerns in the school system or day care where children might fall or cut themselves, is that blood is something to be handled carefully. I remember as a kid we used to cut our skin and become 'blood brothers.' Children do need to be aware that blood is another means of catching somebody else's illness.

"We owe it to children and society to educate them about AIDS because it is a lethal, fatal disease. I don't think it's enough to assume that children will learn about it from their parents or the media. Be explicit without being graphic in the early ages, and I think great care should be taken to provide children with age-appropriate material.

"On the other hand, teenagers would benefit from direct, adult conversation about AIDS. I am particularly concerned about adolescents because their developing sexuality is an integral part of them. How do you say, 'Don't have sex' to a teenager?"

Penelope, thirteen-year-old: "I think the media is blowing AIDS out of proportion. The rates are doubling and doubling making it sound like it's so easy to catch, but it really isn't.

"I think everybody is worrying about it in school, almost like a phobia. I think both parents and school should explain about AIDS. A lot of parents give kids wrong ideas.

"I think AIDS makes people more scared to be around homosexuals, but everybody can get it. I read an article in *Cosmo* about AIDS that said heterosexuals can't get it as easily.

"I'm more worried about the nuclear arms race than AIDS, but I would quit my job if I was a nurse."

Theresa, teacher: "I look at AIDS in relationship to my daughter who is twenty-one. I would never want my daughter to think about AIDS the way I do because my way is haphazard, chancy. If I were to sit with her I would feel like a hypocrite. I would say to her, 'Look, you really have to find out about these men. They could have AIDS.'

"The way I present myself is probably very different from what I am. I present this kind of flip attitude but underneath, I am very shy with men. I would be afraid to hurt them by asking about AIDS.

"It's very hard being in the position of a mother who should guide her child. You can't ignore that AIDS is out there, and you can't assume your children know what it's all about. On the other hand, you have to be very, very careful. Do you say to your children, 'You can't have a sex life,' or 'Do you have a sex life and what do you do?' I don't really say anything to my daughter except, 'Everybody must be really careful these days because of AIDS.' Small talk. Then, I might offhandedly say, 'My God, can you imagine what can happen to somebody?' I end up talking in the third person when I really want to talk directly to my daughter.

"I know my daughter is out there looking for a relationship. I can't be sure but I think it must be very hard for her. She's young and probably more sexual than I am. I don't really know what she does. I know she's not promiscuous. I'm sure she would like to find someone she could care about and feel close to. I would like that for her.

"On the other hand, even if she meets the most charming young man, I worry. How does she know if this guy has AIDS? She doesn't. I was curious when she met a guy a few weeks ago. She only saw him for one evening when she was with a group of friends. They were attracted to each other. He had to return to school before she could see him again. I had such mixed feelings about it because I thought in one way, well, that's life. In another way I thought she probably wouldn't have gotten involved with him anyway. Finally, I felt, isn't it too bad because he was such a lovely boy and wouldn't it have been nice for both of them to have a relationship. I don't even know if she would be sexually active anyway because she might be afraid. I'm very concerned about her.

"It's difficult for me to talk to her about AIDS because of another aspect. At this point, I know that her sexuality is a private issue. I would find it hard to talk about her sexual life while keeping the balance so as to be helpful and educational, without infringing on her privacy. I feel that if I talk to her directly, she might feel guilty about her sex life and I would hate that to happen."

Theresa finds it difficult to be direct when talking to her daughter about AIDS and sexuality, which she feels is a private issue. Each of us must find our own balance and comfort level in order to be helpful when talking to our children about AIDS.

11

AIDS in the Schools

Counselors, helpers, and social workers can learn from the information provided in this chapter when helping women who will undoubtedly have to face similar experiences. Motherhood is a bond common to most women and a story of a mother's struggle to live for her children brings us face-to-face with the heartbreak that is AIDS.

This chapter begins with a true account of an AIDS incident involving a family and a school district as told by a school social worker. Her name is not given, and the names of the boy, family, and school district have been changed to avoid the all-too-common fear, overreaction, and hysteria that continue to plague us despite education about AIDS. The chapter concludes with the story of four high-school girls who had sexual relations with a young man who later died from AIDS. Their dilemma emphasizes the need for more openness in the school and community. My hope is that in the near future we will all not be afraid to speak frankly about the tragedy of AIDS.

Carlos's Story

"I first saw Carlos a year ago as he passed my office, looked in, and smiled at me. He was a thin, brown-skinned boy of eight years whose melancholy smile touched my heart. Several days later he stopped again, this time with a drawing of a birthday present that had a ribbon wrapped around it. A sad, tearful face was drawn on the present. I put the drawing up on my office wall. It was beautifully drawn and I marveled at the talent of an eight-year-old boy.

"As the year progressed, Carlos and I became friends. He would often bring drawings and stop to talk for a few minutes. I learned that his father died when he was four and that he lived with his mother, two older sisters, and a two-year-old brother whom he loved to play with and help care for. When he spoke about his little brother, Sam, it was with pride as he described the feats accomplished by the little boy.

"Our friendship is unusual for an eight-year-old boy and a 43-year-old woman in that it is based on mutual respect that is more typical of adult relationships. When Carlos comes to visit, he always asks how I am or how my day is going. His interest in me is different than that expressed by his peers who are usually more concerned with themselves. This caring quality in Carlos makes him stand out from the other children. He is also very quiet and serious, and there is always a hint of sadness about him. I thought he must have experienced a tragedy in his life (maybe the death of his father?) that makes him appear older than his age. He carries a burden that makes him seem like an old man at times. I would soon learn about this burden.

"A few weeks ago I was asked to talk to two school children whose mother is sick with AIDS. Apparently she is not expected to live long and there is concern for the children who need intensive support and counseling to deal with their mother's illness and imminent death. I was greatly saddened to realize Carlos and his sister were the children I was to talk to. Both were doing poorly in school and were often late or absent. During our talk, the word 'AIDS' was not mentioned. Although I am certain the children know that their mother had AIDS, I wanted to respect their feelings by not mentioning it unless they did. Carlos said his mother is very thin and cannot carry his baby brother, Sam. He helps her watch Sam when he is home and also fills the bottle of water she keeps at her bedside. He also washes the dishes every evening while his sisters do the cooking. Carlos said that his aunts come by every day to see his mother but he resents their intrusion, feeling that they are trying to take the place of his mother. I asked him if he had any questions or concerns with which I could help him. Hesitantly he expressed worry about the possibility of getting sick from eating with his mother or using the same fork. I reassured him that it was not possible to get sick from his mother in that way. All the while I was feeling the terrible burden placed on an eight-year-old boy!

"At the end of our talk I decided to call the children's mother, Maria, in hope of agreement for counseling. On the phone, she was angry, defensive, and requested that I mind my own business. She said she was sick with an intestinal problem. When she hung up I thought that I would not be able to get her agreement for counseling. She needed to give consent and support or her children would not seek help. The next day she called the school and said that I might come to see her and discuss the problems that the children were having in school. At last I had encouragement so that I could hope to convince her to seek help for herself and her children.

"With some trepidation, I drove to Maria's apartment, not wanting to infringe on her privacy and ill health. The main concern was for the children, for whom the school had a certain amount of responsibility in regard to their grades and emotional well-being. The doorbell was answered by an emaciated wraith of a woman who could not have weighed more than sixty pounds. The shades in the apartment were drawn, serving the purpose of making it difficult to see her. Although the apartment was neat and clean, an unpleasant odor prevailed—a smell of sickness. I was asked to sit and Maria defensively asked, 'What is the problem with my children in school?' I responded, 'The children are not doing well in school and normally they are excellent students. I am sure they are worried about you and it's interfering with their performance in school. Don't you think it would be helpful for them to have someone to talk to?' She said, 'My family is very close. I talk to my children and they would tell me if they needed someone else to talk to.' I replied, 'Do they talk to you about their anger and their fear? They love you and don't want to burden you by expressing their true feelings. This is a heavy responsibility for these young children. If you do not give them your support and total agreement to go for counseling, they will not go.' Maria said nothing for a few minutes. Finally she told me how she got sick.

"We sat and talked for an hour. It was eerie sitting with a 32-year-old woman who looked like a living skeleton. She was literally skin and bones—there was no flesh on her frame. I marveled that she could actually be alive and at her fierce pride when talking about her family. I had the sense that sheer will was keeping her alive as she sat straight in her chair, her long, dark hair falling around her shoulders, the only remnant of the beauty she must have **possessed**.

"She said her youngest child was a premature baby that weighed two pounds at birth. It was during the pregnancy that she became sick, revealing the symptoms characteristic of AIDS. Since Sam's birth two years ago, she has been in and out of the hospital every few months when she becomes too weak to function at home. Her husband died four years ago from an AIDS-related illness that she did not specify. Apparently he died in front of her then–eight-year-old daughter who had helped care for him the two years he was ill. The family was devastated. Her husband was an

IV drug user although Maria was not. When he contracted AIDS six years ago, little was known about the disease. Maria unknowingly became infected from her husband and later became pregnant, not realizing the possible fatal implications for herself and her unborn child. She did not even consider an abortion, it was against her religious beliefs.

"Sam has been tested for AIDS antibodies and at this time he tests negative. He is a big healthy-looking two-year old. The contrast between him and his mother is heartbreaking. He is rosy cheeked and bursting with energy, while his mother presents a picture of a sallow skeleton. Her sister comes during the day, when the other children are in school, to help tend to Sam.

"I spoke to Maria's sister, who stays with her children during the more frequent hospitalizations. Her sister, Anna, is twenty-two-years old, has a three-year-old boy and another on the way. She is extremely supportive of Maria and her children. She loves them very much but the tragedy of the illness is becoming too difficult to stand up to. Anna cries whenever she is out of sight of her sister. She worries about Carlos and his sisters. Will they all be able to stay together after Maria dies? Anna has come with her husband from Florida where they were living, to be with her dying sister. Both she and her husband gave up their jobs. She agrees that Carlos and his sisters need counseling. She says that she will talk to Maria to try and convince her to agree but has little hope that it will happen. Maria is protecting her family and doesn't want the community to learn that she has AIDS. She anticipates hostility and fear from her neighbors if they find out the true nature of her illness. Prejudice will be directed toward the children; it has started already from the neighborhood children who have seen how thin Maria is and accuse her of having AIDS. On the school bus, children taunt Carlos with, "Your mother has

AIDS!" The children learn fear from their parents. The children are not to blame. How unfortunate so many people are still so frightened of the disease that they cannot express empathy or give much needed assistance to the tragic family.

"When I left Maria, she said she would ask her children if they wanted to talk to someone outside the family. If they agreed, she would have them contact me in school. I left with an overwhelming sense of sadness. Taking great gulps of fresh air to rid me of the smell of sickness that pervaded the apartment, I drove through the countryside in an attempt to gather strength before returning to school.

"The following day, Carlos came to me and said it was okay for his sister and him to talk to someone. I contacted the local mental health clinic and gave them the go-ahead to call Maria in order to arrange a schedule for the children. Unfortunately, Maria went into the hospital the day that the clinic called to arrange appointments for the children. The clinic suggested that I see the children until the mother returns home and is able to give her approval.

"Carlos is staying with his aunt while his mother is in the hospital. Maria is in Albany, which is several hours from her family. Carlos's older sisters are living at home with another relative who watches Sam until they come home from school. The entire family visited Maria in the hospital this weekend. There are now plans for the family to move to Albany to be near Maria. Although the children are hopeful, it doesn't look as if Maria is coming home.

"Carlos's teacher expresses concern about Carlos and his classmates in regard to the inevitable death of Maria. Should she provide discussion about death and dying to her class? Will it be beneficial or will it evoke fear in the children? Should Carlos not be present when and if the discussion occurs? How can she help Carlos and his classmates to be sensitive and understanding and helpful to one another? These are valid concerns that cannot be addressed until Maria dies. At that time, we can proceed as the need arises. Children are more perceptive than most adults give them credit for being. Because of this unusual sensitivity, we as adults, teachers, and helpers must provide assistance to overcome the issues of AIDS and the loss of a parent. This is a difficult task because adults have many of the same fears and misunderstandings about these topics. Adults also need assistance to deal with fears about AIDS.

"Maria and her family are in a state of denial, which serves the purpose of avoiding confrontation with death and prejudice from the community. The effect this family has on the community and the school system is far-reaching. Denial will only serve its purpose until Maria dies. As of today, both myself and a community social worker are attempting to provide support services to Maria and her family. There is concern from the school: Have the children have been tested for the AIDS virus? Sam, the youngest child, tests negative but will he test positive sometime in the near future? Confidentiality is an issue. How can test results be known when Maria is in the hospital and denying that she has AIDS?

"Teachers are concerned that when the parents of children in Carlos's class find out about the AIDS situation, they will panic and demand knowledge of test results. The school district is attempting to prevent pandemonium before it begins. If the school can prepare answers for the community that will allay fear rather than encourage it, a monumental feat will be accomplished. At least the administration and the teachers involved are supportive of the children and each other. I feel this is the most important preliminary step that has to occur before we can be truly effective in our attempt to deal successfully with the situation. We are presenting a united front to work through a delicate and potentially explosive issue that will affect the children, the school, and the community. I only hope that we will be able to handle it well!

"A few days ago, Carlos came for a visit. We drew pictures together and talked about his mother. Carlos says Maria is 'fine.' She is still in the hospital and Carlos is still staying with his aunt. He only sees his sisters in school and hasn't seen Sam for two weeks. He believes that he and his family will move to Albany within the next few weeks to be near his mother until she is well enough to leave the hospital. If there is a day that Carlos doesn't come to school, I worry. Did his mother die? How will he and his family cope with her death? Do they have a strong enough support system to help them?

"Yesterday, Carlos did not come to school. I was gripped with fear when I called his home. I learned his aunt was sick so Carlos stayed home to watch Sam. Will he come to school tomorrow? I am too attached to Carlos for my own good and will be as devastated as he when Maria dies. I cannot change my feelings nor can I keep Maria from dying. All I can hope to accomplish is to be there for Carlos when he needs help.

"Today, Carlos said he is moving to Albany over the weekend. His aunt, sisters, and Sam will live in a house near the hospital. Carlos doesn't want to leave his friends. He promises to write and I gave him several stamped envelopes with my address. I don't know if I will ever see him again."

As of the time of this interview, Maria was still alive and in the hospital, but I will note that she died one month later. Her children have returned to school and are living with relatives. Although the tragedy of this situation is evident, a positive aspect is the caring people who are involved and willing to help in every way they can. There are others who are less fortunate.

I think it important to point out that AIDS does not occur

in isolation. Everyone is affected. If AIDS occurs in a school, it not only affects the children, teachers, administration, and school board, but it also affects the community. If we still think AIDS hasn't touched us, we are wrong.

Following is an account of an AIDS incident that involves not only the school system, but the community as well. Here is an example of how AIDS reaches all of us. Again, all names have been changed.

John, a twenty-two-year-old man who lived in a small, rural community, died last month of complications from AIDS. He had used IV drugs for several years before his death. He was a handsome man who had an active sex life until realizing he had AIDS, which was about a year before he died. John's intelligence and dark, good looks appealed to the high-school girls, which resulted in frequent sexual encounters.

When John died last month, it was no secret to the community as to the nature of the illness that killed him. One by one, the high-school guidance counselor was approached by several hysterical girls who had sexual relations with John. They were frightened to tell their families and begged advice. Could they get tested without parental consent? This was a new situation for the guidance counselor who didn't readily have the answers. Should he tell the families or the school? Legally and morally, what were the right decisions for him to make?

His first concern was to offer support and calm the girls. Then he called the public-health department to find out about AIDS testing and the need for parental consent for individuals under 18 years old. The health department offers free testing which insures anonymity and counseling. The results take three to four weeks.

The school administration was informed of the plight of the four girls. Support and counseling were provided from the school and the local mental health center until the girls could be tested and the results known. Confidentiality was a major concern to avoid community panic and prejudice.

The four girls were tested and the results were negative for only three. The unlucky girl who tested positive for AIDS antibodies may never develop symptoms of the disease, but this is an uncertainty. She is terrified, and rightly so. Since her relationship with John two years before, she has had two sexual relationships with boys in high school. They must be informed and tested also. With whom have these boys had sex? The AIDS chain continues to reach into the adolescent population of a small community, tragically affecting all who are involved.

Still another sad aspect of this situation involves John's brother, Paul, who is a junior in high school. Paul was so devastated by the death of his brother that he has isolated himself in the heavy use of alcohol. He does not talk to any of his friends, and refuses to go for counseling. His parents are so grief stricken that they cannot help Paul. They need help themselves. No one can make these people seek help so they continue to isolate themselves in their grief, which is a tragedy in itself. In time, the shock and pain of their loss may lessen, and allow the family to support and comfort one another.

This situation brings to the forefront the necessity of awareness of AIDS through massive education both in the schools and the community. Unfortunately, the school in which this incident occurred has not yet begun AIDS education. There is no discussion of AIDS, no posters on the wall to remind of the dangers. Adolescents, whose nature tend toward invulnerability, need special handling when talking about the realities of AIDS. It is not a disease of the aged: anyone can get it. Those who get it can give it to others. AIDS kills: there is no cure.

For further discussion, see the preceding chapter on talking to children about AIDS.

12

Finding Hope

Hope has powerful psychological value, for without it we cannot endure; we have nothing to look forward to. Hope can maintain terminally ill people through long periods of suffering. If there is no possibility of a remission or a cure, what is the purpose of continuing? The role of a counselor can be to provide hope for women who have AIDS or who are involved with others who have AIDS.

It is difficult to believe that anything good can be gained from a time when such a huge number of relatively young people are dying, particularly for those of us who have lost a friend, spouse, child, or relative as a result of AIDS. We are dealing with pain, shock, and outright disbelief that a fatal disease that does not discriminate cannot be cured. We have no concrete answers as to how and why AIDS is here but it is real; we are all affected by it in some way.

There is no doubt that those of us who have not yet become directly involved by knowing someone with AIDS will be in the near future. We need to know how to help ourselves and others when the time comes.

When an elderly parent, friend, or relative dies, it is a natural experience, one that is expected, although painful to the children and friends left behind to cope. This is an order in our life that we become aware of as we grow older. Of course, there are the few unexpected deaths: the son killed in combat during war, the daughter lost in an automobile accident, the infant who dies of SIDS (Sudden Infant Death Syndrome), which are tragic, but rare occurrences that leave a great deal of guilt in their wake.

Never, in our lifetime, has there been a loss of so many young people to a fatal disease.

Growing up, many women experience premature death. I lost two classmates who were killed in separate automobile accidents. One boy was thirteen, the other, sixteen. Disbelief and grief were experienced by the entire class at the funerals. Guilt was involved in the instance of the thirteen-year-old boy who was not well liked by his peers. He was often the brunt of teasing and cruel jokes. A few weeks before he died, a classmate stabbed him in the arm with a pencil, leaving a piece of lead embedded in his upper arm. His loss left an everlasting, guilt-ridden impression for although I was not active in teasing him, I felt I should have supported him more than I did. A heavy burden for a thirteen-year-old who somehow felt responsible for the death of a classmate!

More recently as an adult, I experienced two untimely deaths of friends, both suicides, both men in their early thirties, and both left me with a strong sense of guilt.

The first man, I went to school with in Brooklyn. He took me on my first motorcycle ride. I was so frightened that I kept asking him to go slower. He finally slowed down to the point where he had to put his feet down to keep the motorcycle from tipping over! He respected my fear and, as a result, I always trusted him. I met him again several years later in a therapy group. He was nervous about attending, and came slightly intoxicated. The group ostracized him for his behavior, which resulted in silence and withdrawal on his part. He didn't make it to the third group because he was dead of an overdose of pills. I blamed both myself and the group for his death. Somehow we should have protected and saved him, but weren't able to do so.

The other man was a friend and lawyer, who had recently separated from a relationship and felt put upon by friends who took advantage of his legal expertise without paying for it. He admitted himself into the psychiatric unit of Bellevue Hospital where he remained for two weeks. Upon leaving, he hanged himself. Again, I felt responsible for his death.

I am relating these stories to stress that guilt remains with those left behind who feel responsible for the untimely death.

There is also the tragedy of the loss of hope, both for the victim and the friends or the family of the victim. This is certainly the case today with the monumental loss of young lives to AIDS.

I lost a thirty-nine-year-old cousin to cancer a few years ago. About eight years before she died she had a mastectomy. When recovered from the operation, she and her husband adopted a child fearing they could never have one. Two years after the adoption, she became pregnant and had another child.

She and her family lived a rich, full life on a farm in upstate New York. Neither of them were smokers or heavy consumers of alcohol. When the cancer recurred, this time in her liver, Linda tried every type of chemotherapy, diet, cure. She had hope and the support of her loving family to sustain her for several months. Finally her strength waned and she couldn't fight any longer. She made the decision to have the life-support equipment removed and died shortly after.

What devastated me even more than the tragedy of her untimely death was seeing her parents at the funeral. They were left to cope with this reversed order of death. Weren't they supposed to die before she did? How must it feel to lose one's child? I have imagined the possibility of losing my own daughter, being left behind and alive to continue my life. I don't know if I would be able to bear it but seeing the courage in which my aunt and uncle continued their lives, providing support and comfort to their remaining family, gave me hope as well. If they were able to do it, maybe I could too.

Following are some positive, hopeful outlooks in regard to AIDS from the women who were interviewed, including a longer interview with "Margie," a woman who has AIDS. These responses give hope and inspiration to help ourselves and each other. Counselors, in particular, can benefit by using these experiences to help other women.

Harriet: "I think I actually have more compassion for my friends, period—straight or gay. We're all feeling more vulnerable so therefore, feeling more communicative. AIDS has done that. I still have the friends I had before and still see these friends. Whatever life-style they have, my fear is for my single friends, straight or gay, because they're exposed to just as much. So when people are saying, 'He's gay and let's stay away,' that's a lot of bull! What about the woman who has had many affairs? In the outcome, it's male/female, gay/straight, we're all vulnerable to the same exposures from AIDS.

"I feel more in tune with my friends than before AIDS. It's a confusing time but I find more sheltering and compassion towards others. That's my way of holding on. There's more networking and we're connecting to people we might not have connected with before . . . touching a little more.

"I think for couples this has been an incredible time in that a lot of single friends, straight or gay, will say, 'You couples have been in trouble because you don't network like we do when you need help. As couples, you rely so much on each other, that if one of you gets in trouble, all of the weight is on the other person.' So actually, in a sad way, the single people have more cause to network.

"There is a union happening as a result of AIDS, but what a way to deal with the baby boom!

"Another positive aspect that has come out of AIDS is that before, there was a promiscuity that wasn't mentally healthy. People were dealing with their lives in an indirect, sexual way, and not really facing the reality of love. I think a cleaning up of this kind of avoidant behavior is both physically and emotionally healthy."

Anne: "I've begun to care about myself in a way I never did before AIDS was in the picture. Just to have sex with someone you don't have a committed relationship with is no longer a priority in my life. It could also be the end of my life!

"I guess AIDS has forced me to take a closer look at what I'm doing in regard to relationships. Although I would really like to be with a man and have a wonderful, romantic relationship, I'm now willing to go much more slowly. If I meet someone I'm attracted to I'm certainly not going to hop into bed until I know him well and trust him.

"Before AIDS, I was much more willing to have casual sexual relationships. I don't think this was morally wrong but it was often empty and unfulfilling.

"I think that AIDS has made me look closely at who I am and what I'm doing. I have changed the way I feel about myself because now I have more respect and much more self-esteem. I don't go out drinking anymore because I don't want to put myself in a vulnerable position. After a few drinks my inhibition goes down and my rational thought is cut off. I don't want to tempt fate and put myself in that position anymore.

"So yes, for me something good has come out of this terrible disease. I hope that other women feel the same way. With awareness comes more respect for yourself and your body.

"I was very frightened a few months ago, certain that I had AIDS. I had the test which came back negative. I was relieved to have the chance to continue my life in a more caring and respectful way."

Anne is learning to modify her behavior in regard to interpersonal relationships in order to feel less vulnerable to the threat of AIDS. Her positive outlook brings awareness and increased self-respect. She is taking more control of a potentially dangerous situation so that she can feel safe.

Kathy, a teacher, has some holistic ideas on how to help people who have AIDS. She believes that miracles can happen, and that the physical and spritual aspects of a person cannot be separated.

Kathy: "I believe in a three-step approach to help fight AIDS. First is to clean out the body with a macrobiotic diet which takes all the chemicals and poisons out of the system.

"Second, to cleanse the mind of all negative thoughts that can feed and foster the disease. This takes practice, and a book on higher consciousness can be helpful in learning how to pull it into one's life.

"Finally, spend time every day meditating to help relax. Tension and stress can be eased in the practice of relaxation. One can obtain a book on relaxation techniques or join a class to learn meditation skills.

"I truly believe that this approach can be helpful to people who have AIDS. Positive thinking is an important factor in the curing of disease."

Karen, whose twenty-three-year-old daughter died of an AIDS-related illness, illustrates how hope can come from despair.

Karen's daughter was a drug addict who probably contracted AIDS through the sharing of contaminated needles. When she got sick, her mother and only family member, nursed her at home until she became so ill, hospitalization was necessary. Karen stayed with her daughter in the hospital for two months until she died. During this time, Karen provided physical and emotional support to her daughter who was debilitated by one painful infection after another. They laughed, cried, and got angry together. Their relationship was based on honesty which continued to unite the pair as the end drew near.

Karen never judged her daughter for her drug addiction nor did she deny the horrible reality of the disease that took her daughter's life. Not only did she provide hope and courage for herself and her daughter, but continued to provide support to others with AIDS after her daughter's death. Karen has spent many subsequent hours at hospital beds, bringing hugs or special words to those who have no comfort from family or friends. She has gone on to organize support groups for parents of children with AIDS. In providing hope to others, Karen is doing something to help the fight against AIDS.

San Francisco resident and illustrator, Denise, suggests positive ways in which people can help during the AIDS epidemic.

"Everyone can do something about AIDS and everyone should. The needs are great. Deliver food, become a buddy to someone with AIDS, donate money for research. If we all get together and do what we can, it will result in a strong fight against AIDS."

I agree with Denise in regard to responding to the dangers and horrors of AIDS by doing something beneficial. If we can each take control by doing something, we feel better. This unites us in a common cause to help others. Think of the benefit that comes from many numbers of people helping in whatever way they can. People who can't donate money, can donate their time. I have found other ways in which to help. First, is this book. My hope is that people will read it and gain some knowledge about AIDS that they didn't have before. For people who have AIDS or know someone who has AIDS, my wish is that these shared experiences provide some solace.

Second, I learned about AIDS through workshops and lots of reading, so that I am able to give talks and lectures to others on the topic. Education is a beneficial way in which to reach people. I like to believe that even in a small way, I have helped alleviate the fear and misinformation about this disease.

There are many other things people can do to help. Hospitals and shelters for people who have AIDS are in great need of volunteers who can deliver food, provide companionship (a "buddy system"), and simply be there for those who have no one to be there for them. In hospitals, children with AIDS need someone to spend time with them. These children are in dire need of someone to hug them. More foster homes are needed for children with AIDS whose parents have deserted them. There may be a need for the development of support groups for people with AIDS or for friends, families, and lovers of people, who have AIDS. The Gay Men's Health Crisis can be an important source of assistance to those of you who would like to provide help in any of the previous areas. See appendix A for phone listing.

Without despair, we would have no need for hope. If there were no troubles in the world there would be no reason to hope. But AIDS is here and we can all do something to help. We can be the hope.

This touching example of hope and love comes from a mother whose son and daughter-in-law both have AIDS.

"Yes, my son was a drug user and it broke my heart to see what he was doing to himself. But people on drugs, like alcoholics, can't see what they're doing to themselves or those who love them. I lived with fear and prayed that he would come to see what he was doing to himself and others.

Well, the day came the hard way, and soon drugs were a thing of the past. As for my daughter-in-law, what she did in the past is her past. The past is gone. What we do today is what really matters. She has been like a daughter to me and I love her.

"These two human beings are faced with the most terrifying disease of our day. The fear that takes hold of your heart won't let go. Imagine someone holding a loaded gun to your head and saying you're next. And the anger resulting from all the friends and doctors who have already written them off. These are the things my son and daughter-in-law are facing. What they need is the love and compassion for each other and the understanding of others. A million tears can't wash away the fears, but a few words of love, understanding, and compassion, can be a stepping-stone.

"It's not the end for these two; they have a good chance of beating this thing. The doctors are working around the clock for a cure. They have a fifty-fifty chance and as long as they hold onto each other, encourage each other, and do as the doctors tell them, they are going to make it, with God's grace. If my love or tears could cure them they would be the healthiest people on earth. I pray that my love and the love of others will see them through."

Gay activist Cleve Jones, who is infected with the AIDS virus but displays no symptoms, has found a way out of the despair of losing a lover and many friends to AIDS. His inspiration and hope have been the origination of the Names Project, a memorial quilt made of patches bearing the names of men, women, and children who have died in the AIDS epidemic. In *USA Today* (December 7, 1987), Jones says, "You can't allow yourself to despair because if you do, then you lose everything. We must bear it and go on with our lives. To love and go on and make a difference. What's happening here is very moving in a positive way.

Out of this grief a lot of very courageous and loving people are emerging. As bad as it is, I still feel privileged to be part of it."

Cleve Jones, you've said it all.

Margie

Following, is an interview with a woman who has AIDS. Her courageous battle against the disease brings inspiration and hope to all who come to know her. She requests to be known only as "Margie" because she has an eight-year-old daughter who does not know of her illness. Although she says she is honored to be a part of this book, I am honored to have spoken with her.

"I believe in God and I believe He's keeping me alive for a reason. I think that reason is to help others. I just can't take this lying down and only sitting back anymore.

"I was diagnosed with AIDS seven years ago. I was a drug addict for seventeen years. When my daughter was born eight years ago, I started getting sick. I was admitted into the hospital for problems with internal blood clotting. At that time, I was diagnosed with a low platelet count. I was in and out of hospitals for about four years and diagnosed with having eleven different diseases that included Hodgkin's disease, Crohn's disease, and leukemia. I had operations, exploratories, biopsies—always for some problem with my lymph nodes, and I was very sick for a long time.

"Somewhere in the middle of all these hospitalizations, the doctor told me I had AIDS. I had only started hearing about AIDS because it was new at that time. I remember the doctor walking into the room, telling me I had AIDS, and walking out. He was a cold person and I didn't like him at all. He kept treating me for blood disorders but never said anything about the disease. I also told my family that I had AIDS, but they went into denial. Then I went into denial and got into drug addiction even worse.

"I would go into the hospital for six weeks at a time. I tried not to think about anything, but between drugs and AIDS, it was too much. Being a drug addict you feel slimy enough. I had no self-esteem or self-worth. Toward the end of my drug addiction, I really hit bottom. I wanted to die. Every time I was put in the hospital for another infection, I would think, "Oh good, maybe now this is the one that will kill me."

"I was just hanging around waiting to die. There were times in the hospital that they put me down at the end of the hall, in isolation. Especially in those days when AIDS was still so new. Nobody wanted to come near me. The nurses didn't want to come in my room. They would leave my food tray out in the hallway and I'd be too sick to get up and get it. I'd have to wait until somebody from my family would come to bring my tray so I could eat.

"I always felt toxic. I wasn't that educated about AIDS. All I knew was what I heard on the news, and that wasn't much. I thought I could give it to my daughter if she drank out of the same glass. I was a nursery-school teacher and loved kids but I was too scared to go near them. My girl friend had just had a baby and asked me to be the godmother. I said no because I was afraid if I picked up the baby, he would get sick and die.

"Finally, after a long time, I wasn't dying and I wanted to. I felt as if I were walking in a living death. I was detoxed a few times and went to AA but I hit bottom and ended up in jail. In jail I was put in an isolated cell where nobody would come near me. I felt less than human.

"From jail, I was sent to a hospital because I got so sick. I had a new doctor who tried to get me into a rehab program but nobody would take me. Finally, after 21 days, I got in and learned that I had TB, which is one of the opportunistic infections that people with AIDS can get. In rehab, they wouldn't let me talk about AIDS or any of my feelings. I was feeling very bad about myself and thought I was so toxic and inhuman that nobody wanted to come near me. I went into denial again because I didn't know what else to do. I was able to put the AIDS issue on the shelf for a while. I call it a healthy denial because I concentrated on getting healthy, clean, and sober.

"Since I got clean, I started going to AA. I started feeling healthy and gained 40 pounds. I had chronic diarrhea for two years prior to this and weighed only 90 pounds. Before this, I couldn't walk because of operations on veins in my legs. I could only use crutches to get around.

"After a couple of months of rehab and feeling good, I got a job teaching nursery school again. I was still in denial and thought I really didn't have AIDS. At the time I was first diagnosed, there was no blood test, so I thought they made a mistake because I felt too healthy to have AIDS. I continued to do well but I still kept getting sick a lot. I thought it was because I was around kids again, who always have a cold or something, not because I had AIDS. I had pneumonia three times, strep throat, and I got the chicken pox again!

"I decided to be tested again to see if I really did have AIDS. I went to the health department to get the test. While I was waiting for the results, my doctor said, 'Margie, you've been tested by us many times since 1985. Don't get your hopes up that the results will be negative this time.' Last August [of 1987] I was tested and the results were positive.

"I then went to Rockland County to a specialist because I was always getting thrush in my mouth, and yeast and skin infections. I was still feeling pretty well. When I was at Rockland, I was diagnosed with ARC that showed activity. Because of my white blood count, I was able to start a treatment program. It was only last year that I really started to deal with the disease. I started to fight back.

"My first reaction was, 'Okay, I have AIDS and I'm going to do something about it. I need help—some counseling or something.' I started going to different agencies all over Dutchess County to look for a support group but there was nothing. Doors kept slamming in my face so I stopped looking. I told a few close friends that I had AIDS. Although I was going to AA, I didn't have the courage to talk about my feelings to the other people there except for my close friends who were my support system. I was finally able to share my feelings at an AA meeting one night. It was a risk and I had some bad reactions, but most people didn't turn away. I've even gotten closer to them because I talked about AIDS. These people have continued to love and support me unconditionally.

"After being sober, off drugs, and from the love of these people, I've gotten my self-esteem back. My health is back too. I recently started my own support group with a friend. We have a hot-line number at which people can call and talk. I also started another support group at a nearby monastery. I do whatever I can to help others with the disease.

"Today I am healthy and I believe the treatment is really helping. I know that some of the infections I get, like thrush, are stress related. When I get tired, I know I'm doing too much so I take it easy and rest a little. I try to keep active and I've gained 40 pounds that I would like to lose! My doctor tells me not to worry about the weight. I do self-healing exercises and play meditation tapes every night before I go to sleep. I have to keep a positive attitude and be close to my support system.

"I have a lot of human contact today and get lots of hugs. I'm not rejected like I used to be when I was on drugs. The love I get and give has a lot of healing power. I'm not saying that I'm not going to die, but I don't see it happening too soon. I have a lot of hope about living and doing the right thing. When I go home and lie down at night I think that if I didn't wake up one morning, it would be okay.

"The quality of my life has changed completely. It's not that I'm grateful that I have AIDS, but I have gotten spirituality and a higher power that I call God. It's amazing how many doors have opened to me because of this disease. I have the support groups and the people that I'm meeting from all over the country, who are in the same situation. I have a special closeness to other people that I never had before. There is a friend who I've never met. We only talk on the phone but we feel like best friends that share a real intimacy. We have this disease in common. This is the way with everyone I meet now—automatic intimacy. It's wonderful.

"You asked about my daughter. She lives with her father's parents but I see her every weekend. She's lived with them since I was in and out of the hospital because I couldn't take care of her. It's working out real well. I'm on SSI and baby-sit to make some extra money in case I get sick and have to go into the hospital again.

"Right now, I'm going to therapy to talk about my daughter. I'm trying to write her a letter to tell her how I feel. I might not give it to her but it's a way to help deal with it. I don't know if I should or shouldn't tell her, but I don't want her to find out some other way. This is the one issue that's really hard for me now.

"About her father—he tested negative and so did someone I lived with for seven years. They were both tested last year. This is why I like to tell my story. I have a positive attitude, not about dying, but about living with the disease. If I can bring this message, especially the fact that I've tested positive for seven years and am still alive and healthy, I can give people hope that AIDS doesn't always mean devastation. Living with AIDS is hard because of the way society is. That's why I give talks and presentations—to try to change people's attitudes. If I talk to these people with a good attitude, it affects them in a good way. If I allow them to get to know me, to show I'm a nice person, it turns people around and lets them see AIDS in a different light."

Margie is helping and bringing hope by talking to people about AIDS, by providing a support system to others in need. Her courage should be a model for us all.

Appendix
Organizations for Information on AIDS

National

Centers for Disease Control
Hotline: 1-800-342-AIDS
(Recorded information)
1-800-447-AIDS (Specific
information)
In Atlanta: (404) 329-1290
(Recorded information)
(404) 329-1295 (Specific
questions)
(404) 329-3534 (Printed
material)

National Institute of Allergy
and Infectious Diseases
Office of Research Reporting
and Public Response
(301) 496-5717

Public Health Service
1-800-342-AIDS (Recorded
information)
1-800-447-AIDS (Specific
questions)

American Association of
Physicians for Human
Rights
P.O. Box 14366, San
Francisco, CA 94114
(415) 673-3189

National Gay and Lesbian
Task Force
1517 U St., NW, Washington
DC 20009
(202) 332-6483
Fund for Human Dignity
(212) 741-5800 (Educational
material)
National Gay and Lesbian
Crisis Line
1-800-221-7044 (Crisis
counseling)

National Hemophilia
Foundation
Soho Building

110 Greene Street, Room 406, New York, NY 10012 (212) 219-8180

National Association of People with AIDS (202) 483-7979 (Health care referrals)

National Lesbian and Gay Health Foundation P.O. Box 65472, Washington DC, 20035 (202) 797-3708 (Health care referrals)

United States Conference of Mayors 1620 I Street, NW, 4th Floor Washington DC, 20006 (202) 293-7330 (Directory of AIDS Related Services)

World Wide

World Health Organization AIDS Program, Geneva, Switzerland Hotline: 91-21-11

World Health Organization AIDS Program, Europe, Copenhagen, Denmark Hotline: 290-111

State Departments of Health

Alabama—(205) 261-5131
Alaska—(907) 561-4406
Arizona—(602) 255-1203
Arkansas—(501) 661-2395
California—(916) 445-0553
Colorado—(303) 331-8320
Connecticut—(203) 549-6789
Delaware—(302) 995-8422
District of Columbia—(202) 332-AIDS
Florida—(904) 488-2905
Georgia—(800) 342-2437
Hawaii—(808) 735-5303
Idaho—(208) 334-5944
Illinois—(312) 871-5696
Indiana—(317) 633-8406
Iowa—(515) 281-5424

Kansas—(913) 862-9360
Kentucky—(502) 564-4478
Louisiana—(504) 342-6711
Maine—(207) 289-3747
Maryland—(301) 945-AIDS
Massachusetts—(617) 727-0368
Michigan—(517) 335-8371
Minnesota—(612) 623-5414
Mississippi—(601) 354-6660
Missouri—(816) 353-9902
Montana—(406) 444-4740
Nebraska—(402) 471-2937
Nevada—(702) 885-4988
New Hampshire—(603) 271-4487
New Jersey—(609) 588-3520

New Mexico—(505) 984-0911
New York—(518) 473-0641
North Carolina—(919) 733-3419
North Dakota—(701) 224-2378
Ohio—(614) 466-4643
Oklahoma—(405) 271-4061
Oregon—(503) 229-5792
Pennsylvania—(717) 787-3350
Rhode Island—(401) 277-2362

South Carolina—(803) 734-5482
South Dakota—(605) 773-3364
Tennessee—(615) 741-7247
Texas—(512) 458-7504
Utah—(801) 538-6191
Vermont—(802) 863-7240
Virginia—(804) 786-6267
Washington—(206) 361-2914
West Virginia—(304) 348-5358
Wisconsin—(608) 267-3583
Wyoming—(307) 777-7953

New York

Gay Men's Health Crisis
P.O. Box 274
132 West 24th Street
New York, NY 10011
(212) 807-6655

Gay Men's Health Project
74 Grove Street, #2J
New York, NY 10014
(212) 691-6969

New York City Department
of Health
Office of Gay and Lesbian
Concerns
125 Worth Street, #806
New York, NY 10013
Offices: (212) 566-6110
Hotline: (718) 485-8111

AIDS Council of
Northwestern New York
Albany, NY
(518) 445-AIDS

Children and Youth AIDS
Project
New York, NY
(212) 807-6655

Mid-Hudson Valley AIDS
Task Force
White Plains, NY
(914) 723-6520